To: Ralph + B

With best regard

The Nana In The Chair, And the tales she told

An anecdotal biography of Mary Dunne Ware (1860-1956)

By

Edward C. McManus

This book is a work of fiction. Places, events, and situations in this story are purely fictional. Any resemblance to actual persons, living or dead, is coincidental.

© 2004 by Edward C. McManus. All rights reserved.

No part of this book may be reproduced, stored in a retrieval system, or transmitted by any means, electronic, mechanical, photocopying, recording, or otherwise, without written permission from the author.

First published by AuthorHouse 06/14/04

ISBN: 1-4184-5768-X (e-book)
ISBN: 1-4184-4806-0 (Paperback)

Library of Congress Control Number: 2004094714

This book is printed on acid free paper.

Printed in the United States of America
Bloomington, IN

Cover photo: This is Nana Mary Dunne Ware sitting in her room beside the cathedral radio my father gave her in 1939. The radio was her constant companion and her lifeline to the outside world. She had the dial memorized and would move through the voice, music, and static to find her programs. I spent many an evening beside her listening to my programs after her supper hour of religious programs had concluded.

I took this photograph on May 13, 1953 at approximately 4pm. Nana had just finished her afternoon tea and was telling me a story.

Above: This is the white house at 102 Temple Street in Fitchburg, Massachusetts where all the little stories and minor adventures took place. It was built by my grandfather Felix in the 1920's and was my father Leo's pride and joy. It was a big, comfortable, and happy home filled with family, friends, barking dogs, stories, and laughter.

Back cover: This is the Ed & Judy McManus family. Front row: Jon and Julia. Second row: Ed, Kerry, Judy, Kevin, Lilly, Tim. Third row: Mary, Ed Jr., and Kim. You'll meet the four grandchildren again in Nana's tale of "The 120th Stair of Blarney Castle." They were known in those days and in those parts, among the Little People, as Lord Kevin of the Glenn, Queen Julia, Good Jonathan, and the Princess Lilly.

1968: The family gets together. Back row from left, Leo F. McManus, Sr., Patricia McManus (Leo Jr.'s wife), Marcy McManus (George's Wife), Mary (McManus) Morin and husband Paul H. Morin, Kathryn R. (Ware) McManus, Leo F. McManus, Jr.

Front row: Author Edward C. McManus and wife Judy McManus, George J. McManus, and Aunt Fanny Ware (star of "Nana, Aunt Fanny, and Life in the Mills").

Nana Dunne Ware: Genealogy and Dates:

Nana Mary Dunne was born on March 21, 1860 in Lixnaw, County Kerry, Ireland. She was christened Mary Kathryn Agnes Dunne (the family name had an "e" when used in Ireland; but it was dropped when the family moved to the United States). Her parents were Michael Dunne (1817 - 1881), and Mary Kate Davis Dunne (1816 - 1878). Neither of them ever came to America. They died in Ireland.

Nana's paternal grandparents were Timothy Dunne and Catherine Conway. Her maternal grandparents were Edward Davis and Margaret Thornton. I don't have dates on these people, but we can assume they were born in the late 1700's and lived on into the first half of the 1800's.

Nana came to America in 1883, after her father died, to honor a promise she had made to him. She came to Fitchburg, Massachusetts to live with her father's brother, Timothy Dunne. Her uncle Tim advanced her the $30 it cost to come across steerage and brought her to his home where she worked off the debt by caring for his crippled son, Young Tim. Her stories suggest that the boy had polio, or infantile paralysis as it was called then. It took her two years to work off the $30 debt, but she lived with the Dunne's all that time. They were kind to her, treated her as part of the family, and she had no regrets.

On September 3, 1885, she married George H. Ware. Coincidentally, he too was from Lixnaw although they knew each other only by sight in the village. They met again in Fitchburg at one of her uncle Timothy Dunn's Sunday Tea Socials that he held for recent Irish arrivals. It was a place to meet new friends, network, find a job, and generally get comfortable with their new American setting. Perhaps most importantly, they could accomplish this among the local Irish who had been here for a while and were sympathetic to their problems and needs. I have her wedding band. She put it aside for me and I wore it when I married my wife Judy in 1959. So far it's worked its way through two long marriages. Coincidentally, Judy wore her grandmother's wedding band too. That was Nana Ellen Toomey, mother of Judy's mother Lillian Toomey Pierce. We plan to pass these rings on to another generation.

George Henry and Mary Dunne Ware were the parents of Michael A. Ware (born 1886), George H. Ware, Jr. (1888), Charles Ware (1898), Thomas C. Ware (1890), Mary (May) Ware Beauvais (1893), and my mother, Kathryn Rose Rita Ware McManus (1904)

Nana Dunne Ware died on her 96th birthday in March of 1956. She spent only the last few months in a nursing home after suffering a fall. She maintained her faculties to the very end of her life.

Table of Contents

Introduction

These are little stories, told to a little boy, by a loving old woman who had no wealth or property so she gave him her time, attention, and love. As every sane person knows, there is no greater gift.

I was the little boy. The stories were told to me in the 1940's when we all lived together in the white house on Temple Street. Some of the stories come from the 19th century when Nana, the heroine of my story, was a little girl in Lixnaw, County Kerry, Ireland. Other stories come from her adventures in America during the late 1800's and early 1900's.

"Ireland," Charles Haughey wrote, "is where strange tales begin and happy endings are possible." That pretty well summarizes Nana's stories.

Nana Mary Dunne Ware was born in 1860. Let's put that into perspective. She shared a birth year with Annie Oakley. She was born before Abraham Lincoln was elected president of the United States. She was 11 years old in 1871 when Wild Bill Hickock cleaned up Abilene, and 16 years old in 1876 when George Armstrong Custer made his Last Stand at Little Big Rock. She was 40 when the new century began in 1900 and 43 when the Wright Brothers first flew at Kitty Hawk in 1903. She was already 55 when World War I broke out in 1915. She was 80 when she came to live with us in the white house on Temple Street.

Nana told these stories sixty and more years ago and none of them were written down until now. If there are errors of fact and place, they are mine not her's. She knew what she was talking about. Also, I admit to filling in a few parts to help flesh out the story, but even the additions are consistent with what Nana said. They may be things I've heard or read or even half remembered fragments from other stories she told at other times.

I have never been to Ireland. My knowledge of the land and its people, even the village of Lixnaw, come from the stories I heard as a boy over a half century ago. Even then those stories were old. Nana left Ireland in the 1880's so we are talking about things that happened over one hundred and twenty years ago in a place I have never visited, and which were never written down until the 21st Century. That doesn't make for journalistic precision—but I think it is in the best tradition of story telling and demonstrates how oral history comes down to us over the years.

I call my book, **The Nana In The Chair** because that is the name given her by my sister Mary's children, the Morin's. They called her that to distinguish her from my own Mother, whom they called Nana. My Nana Ware was their great grandmother so it is appropriate that she have a great and grand name all her own. My brother Leo liked it too and suggested I use it as the title of this collection.

There is no certified history here, no serious revelations, no claims of originality or gospel truth (although every story here is based on truth), and there are no great lessons to be drawn. The purpose of the stories today is the same as it was then: To entertain. If anybody gets a lesson out of it too, let that be a grand bonus from Nana Ware.

I hope you are entertained as much by Nana's stories as I was, and as were the other people who were lucky enough to be with her, know her and talk with her. She was quite the neighborhood celebrity. There were many people over the years, family and friends, who went out of their way to tell me how much they benefited from knowing Nana Ware.

Let me close this introduction with my own version of an Irish toast:

To Nana and to you:

May your grandchildren remember you with equal affection.

References and Acknowledgements

First of all, I need to thank everyone in the family who helped out by remembering a story. Brother Leo remembered his share and contributed much detail to flesh out both the stories and the details of Nana's approach to life. Brother George was helpful too—although he earnestly maintains he was at work or doing chores when the rest of the family sat down to tell stories. He remembered fewer of Nana's sayings than I do. I tell both of my brothers: "See? You didn't *listen*!" Of course I must remember Cousin Peggy (Beauvais) Carnavale who, as official family historian, knows everything there is to know about the Wares and where they came from. Too many of the other cousins and family members, like my own sister Mary, are gone now—but I think they've been with me on this project in their own way. They'd be with Nana Ware now, and she'd probably send them along to make sure the job was done properly.

My parents, Leo & Kathryn McManus, are gone too—but the values and memories they gave us all in the White House on Temple Street will stay with us for as long as we live. All of the uncles and aunts are gone too. All are warmly remembered.

Thanks too to my wife Judy and the family members who have endured many drafts of this effort and favored me with criticism—nearly all of it constructive. A special thanks to Judy's mother, Nana Lillian (Toomey) Pierce. She is 93 at this writing and sharp as a bell. Her own mother, Nana Ellen Toomey, was a contemporary of Nana Ware and used many of the same expressions. She helped recall and define many of my "Nana-isms."

I have been reading books about Ireland, its people, and their stories for well over sixty years now. It started with the excellent readers the nuns gave us in Catholic grammar school (in my case, St. John's School of Sacred Heart Parish in West Fitchburg, Massachusetts). We were given a new reader each year and every book had lyric and narrative poems, short stories and essays, and a short novel. The stories weren't all about Ireland, but many of them were—and they were all upbeat, positive, and thought provoking. Those readers began a love affair with the written word for me just as Nana's stories began one with the spoken word.

The best book on the Irish subject of Irish ghost stories was one I read in the early 1950's—and it was old then (copyright in the 1880's). It was called, "Short Irish Ghost Stories: Half Hours With Irish Authors". It was filled with some of the most chilling, and funny, Irish ghost stories I ever read. I'll run across it one day in a used bookstore, or on the web, and renew my acquaintance with these gifted writers.

In the course of this book I consulted a variety of sources to get it all right. It was important to me that the "look and feel" (as the software gurus say) be just right. My first impression was amazement at the number of Irish folk and fairy tales that are in print going back to the early 1800's. Part of this, I think, is due to the oral tradition of the Scots, Welsh and Irish who inhabited different parts of that island world—but traveled freely one among the others. Welsh stories became Irish and Irish became Scottish and around and around it went until it ended up in one happy blend of tales that, like Nana's songs, had a common root among the differing cultures. I found many stories about the Leprechauns, Fin McCoul (or McCool), the grand Irish giant, Blarney Castle and the like. While they were not exactly Nana's tales, they were recognizable and who is to know which of them came first. The libraries are full of such books and each of them offers a special reading joy of its own. The interested reading pilgrim will find hours of entertainment available for the asking.

These are the books I used for fact verification, background, reference, and inspiration. They are in no particular order:

1. *Irish Fairy and Folk Tales*, edited by William Butler Yeats, and published sometime in the 1890's. My version was a Random House Modern Library edition that came out in the early 1950's. The poet Yeats comments on the Irish tales and his explanations are as much fun as the stories themselves.

2. *Irish Sagas and Folk Tales,* by Eileen O'Faolain, published 1954 and 1982 by Avenel Books and distributed by Crown Publishing. Here you will find the classic Irish stories of myth and fable told in modern English.

3. *Myths and Legends of Ireland (Tales Of A Magical and Mysterious Past)* by Ronald Pearsall, published by Todtri Productions, 1996. This big picture book is an excellent backgrounder to the stories of Ireland. It tells the old stories and shows modern color photographs of the sites along with contemporary line drawings and representations from ancient sources.

4. *Castles, Keeps, and Leprechauns (Tales, Myths, and Legends of Historic Sites in Great Britain and Ireland* by Phyllis Meras, published by Congdon & Weed, Inc., 1988. This "Traveler's Companion" contains some 500 short anecdotes about interesting historical sites in Great Britain and Ireland. Did you know that in Fortingall Churchyard, Pontius Pilate was born under a yew tree to a Caledonian tribeswoman and a Roman envoy? You will learn this and more if you read the book!

5. *Isle Of The Shamrock,* by Clifton Johnson, published by The MacMillan Company, 1901. This little travel book records a tour of Ireland undertaken by Mr. Johnson on foot sometime around 1900. It is a wonderful background book. He tells grand tales about all the adventures he had walking the country side, meeting the people, staying in their homes, and visiting their schools, churches, and places of work. He tells what they thought, said, and did. I loved his story of the country girl who went to work as

a maid in a big house in the city. She was told never to go into a certain room upstairs, it was for men only. For days she watched as men went in, but never came out. One night her curiosity got the better of her. She found a key and let herself into the room with a candle for light. The room seemed empty, until her eyes grew accustomed to the dark. She saw that the tables were covered with human heads impaled on spikes. She fainted dead away. Later it was explained she had entered a private barbershop that had one way in and another way out. The human heads were wig holders. Her curiosity was forever stilled that day.

6. *Ireland,* by Lillian Fox Quigley, published by the McMillan Company, 1961. This is a wonderfully readable history of Ireland from megalithic times to the present. Here I learned about the English cavalry horses, and how most of them came from Ireland. How under the English Penal Laws, no Irishman could own a horse worth more than five pounds—regardless of its market value. Any English citizen could demand that the Irishman sell him his horse for that five pound amount—and it would carry the force of law. She relates how the people in the Irish Diaspora would visit St. Kierman's grave at the Monastery of Clonmacnoise (545 AD) on the River Shannon near Athalone and take a handful of dirt from his grave before sailing for America. A pinch of that earth tossed overboard, they believed, would calm a stormy sea.

Finally, thanks to all the friends and acquaintances that helped out by contributing stories and memories of their own Irish parents and grandparents. Sometimes I felt I was editing a collection of "told stories" as opposed to creating something original. I will settle for the credit due to the one who pulled it all together and put it in one place. As Nana would say when we returned from a Sunday afternoon outing in the old Packard, "It was a grand ride."

Growing Up With Nana Ware

It was the 1940's in Fitchburg, Massachusetts, a paper mill town located 50 miles west of Boston. We lived in the big white house my grandfather built at 102 Temple Street in West Fitchburg, Massachusetts. We moved there from Milk Street in 1939 when Grandpa Felix McManus died and my father, Leo, by now the only surviving heir, inherited the house and property. I was two years old, so it is really the first home I remember.

My brothers Leo and George remember the first time they saw the house after Grandpa Felix died in 1939. They drove up one evening with my father in his 1937 Chevrolet Special Deluxe. The house was locked and inside was Grandpa's great Collie, Prince. He and Grandpa had lived there alone for years and he was a one-man dog, fiercely loyal to his owner and no one else. When my father unlocked the back door, the dog lunged at him unexpectedly and, if it weren't for Dad's quick reflexes in pulling the door shut, he would have had a major dog bite somewhere on his body. Dad never lost his cool. He walked out to the garage and returned to the house carrying a long handled iron shovel. George and Leo heard a large *bonk,* and then Dad called them in to join him. Prince was unconscious on the kitchen floor. My father said, "He'll be fine. He just had to learn who the boss is." The dog was fine after that, and easy to live with too. It gave my brothers even more respect and awareness of who was the boss in our family.

The Temple Street house was a good-sized eight-room white cape with a full cellar and attic and a two-car cinder block garage. It was situated just below Sacred Heart Church, near the woods owned by Crocker-Burbank Inc., the company that ran most of the paper mills in town. The woods were perfect places to walk, see nature first hand, and play everything from hide and go seek to cops and robbers. The woods were beautiful throughout the four seasons of the year.

Mary, Leo, George, and I attended St. John's Grammar School, which was just up the hill, near Sacred Heart Church. It was staffed by the Sisters of the Presentation who took a no nonsense approach to education. Years later an educator who had himself been through Catholic schooling said the great lesson he had learned from the nuns was never to underestimate fear and intimidation as teaching aids. If you've been there, you know what he meant. The message was prayer, work, and duty. We didn't spend a lot of time on entitlements and rights. However, although the curriculum was suffused with Catholic themes and almost sublimal messages about the Faith, we were not required to tow the line in mindless acceptance of everything we were taught. We were encouraged to think and to discuss. Not argue, discuss. That was almost as good. We were also encouraged to pursue higher education. I remember that by fifth grade the nuns were telling us that people who graduated from college could expect to earn over a quarter of a million dollars more in their fifty year working lifetime than the average high school graduate. That was a great fortune, to be sure. And—to the end of preparing for that higher education, they kept us busy with in-class studies and after school homework.

It was much the same at home. Everyone had something useful to do. By the fourth grade I had been assigned an important family job. I came home from St. John's at 3:30PM each day - just in time to prepare and have tea with Nana Ware. The menu was always the same: Strong tea with milk and sugar (she pronounced it "tay"), and buttered Graham crackers. "A cuppa tay," she'd say, "and me crackers." The conversation was always different.

Sometimes I would provide the entertainment. I would have to tell something of interest that happened to me during the day ("Make a little story out of it," she would say), or read a piece or a poem from my school reader. Nana liked that. I could see her absorbing the fresh material into her repertoire, mentally tailoring it to fit her style, and then filing it away for later use in one of her own wonderful tales.

If I didn't have my school reader, local gossip was always good, and neighborhood goings-on were of particular interest. She clucked sympathetically when I told her that Mary Forbes' clothesline broke and her entire Monday wash fell into the mud. "A day's work lost," she said sadly, identifying with a trying domestic tragedy as only someone can who has been through it themselves.

Most often Nana did the talking. She told stories. Sometimes they were stories from the old days. There was the time my grandfather lost a dollar on the way home from work, and how the two of them and the children rushed out to trace his path and find it before the darkness set in. They never found it. A dollar was one-tenth of his weekly take-home wage. In my own time, I had seen the men coming home on payday after a week's work in the mills. I knew that they often stopped at the Log Cabin Cafe (known locally as "The Beer Joint") for a little liquid refreshment. Some of my friends' mothers used to walk to the mill paymaster's office each week and collect their husbands' pay—all cash in a little brown envelope. Thus they made sure the money was not "lost" on the way home. I always wondered if there was more to grandfather's story than he let on to his wife. I kept that thought to myself.

She liked jokes. Her favorite was about the Irishman getting off the boat in Boston when the fire brigade thundered by. The horses' hoofs pounded a tattoo on the cobblestones as the boiler shot off sparks and steam, and the clanging bells drove everyone out of their path. "God in Heaven, what is that?" his friend asked. "I think they're moving Hell," answered the Irishman, "and the first load just went by."

My mother said that jokes were an important part of her life at home as a child too. "Once," she told me, "around 1915, my father was reading his paper on a Sunday afternoon and I asked him, 'Pa, what is the heaviest thing in the world?'

'Why, I don't know, Kitty,' he said. 'What is it?'

I said, 'S**t! Even an elephant can't hold it!'

"Now I don't know where I got such a story, but Pa was not amused. He chased me all around the house calling out the scandal of my saying such a word to my father, let alone saying it on the Lord's Day. Finally, he gave up the chase and sat back in his chair and just laughed and laughed. Your Nana Ware came in and asked what the entire disturbance was about on a Sunday afternoon. 'It's just your daughter,' Pa told her, 'acting too much like her mother.'"

Sometimes Nana spoke of The Great War or World War I as we know it today. She had four sons, Mike, George, Charley, and Tom and at least two of them were in it. Charlie was in the Balloon Corps. They used hot air balloons to fly over the battlefield to observe and report back enemy movement by carrier pigeon. Enemy sharpshooters and fighter planes would try to puncture those balloons. The trick was to get out of the way as quickly as possible, land the balloon fast, - or jump. "The last alternative," said Uncle Charlie "was always the last alternative."

Uncle George was in the infantry—the famous 25th Yankee Division. They both went off to the Western Front in France to fight the Kaiser, a man Nana seriously despised for threatening her boys. "Your mother Kathryn and her sister May would bring me pictures of the Kaiser from the newspapers. 'Here he is, Ma.'" they'd say, "and I'd grind my thumb into his eye." I felt she suspected the girls enjoyed this little display of righteous outrage from their otherwise kind-hearted mother.

She never understood World War II. "We fought the Great War to end all wars," she would say. "What in God's name are we fighting again for?" This time it was her grandsons who were being threatened. It all seemed like a horrible and avoidable replay of what she went through earlier in the century.

Although she was blind now, she was still fascinated by electricity and how it powered the light and the heat and the cathedral table radio my father had given her. She had memorized all the radio stations on the dial and spent the day twitching the knobs, as my mother put it, and listening to her soap operas. I remember "Stella Dallas" and "Ma Perkins", audience shows like "Queen For A Day", and "Don McNeill's Breakfast Club". Don was tops for good conversation. Late afternoons and evenings, however, were dedicated

4

to her Catholic religious programs. The rosary, novenas, the Sacred Heart Hour, the evening Mass - all of them she listened to in their turn. She sang and prayed along with them, occasionally talking back to the radio if the priest went too fast, or said something she did not agree with. She liked to have me sit with her and listen - but it was not my favorite way to spend a lot of time. However, if I did stay, the radio was mine for the last hour before bedtime and I could hear "The Lone Ranger" or "Edgar Bergen and Charlie McCarthy". Nana listened and laughed along with me.

She told me how she had seen the first electric light in Fitchburg. She had walked into town on a summer's night with her uncle and the family she worked for. There was to be a lighting demonstration in the center of town and a party atmosphere prevailed. There was a band and speakers and refreshments. When the sun went down, the mayor gave a little speech she didn't remember, and then flipped a switch. An electric bulb flashed on from a vantage point atop the third story roof of one of the highest buildings in town. The crowd ooh'd and aah'd like they do at fireworks displays, and watched it for a long time before they broke up and made their way home. Her uncle was not impressed. "How will they get those ugly, fat wires that carry the electricity into our homes," he asked. "Run them through the trees? People won't tolerate it. It's just another costly toy." Others, she remembered, feared that the electricity would leak out from the electrical sockets, and God only knows what leaking electricity might do. It was just one more thing people didn't need, couldn't afford, and would have to worry about.

Speaking of lights, there were regular blackouts during World War II. On certain evenings all lights had to be turned off after dark so that no signal would be displayed to help guide the enemy bombers that, Thank God, never came. I knew Nana was blind; we had an ironclad family rule against moving furniture around. However, it still amazed me that in the winter evenings with the lights turned off she could move around the house as surely and quickly as she did during the day. She was a marvel to watch. Humming her little tunes, she would shuffle from room to room avoiding the parlor Baldwin piano and Crosley radio console, the dining room table, even my father's footstool near his chair. More than once I had my friends in to see her in action. They thought it was a great gift. She enjoyed the attention. She would say, "The blind have the advantage in the dark."

Her life was filled with her music and she sang constantly. I wish I could remember all the old songs she sang, as I fear many of them will be lost forever. I have checked old books and record shops and though I found a few of them, most are not recorded either in print or sound. I wrote down the few that I memorized from hearing them so many times. They are in this book. There was the love song, "Barney Mavourneen." The historical novelty, "With My Bonnie Bunch of Flowers," - which my father thought was far too racy for my young ears. And "Erin Go Bragh', which she sang in a very assertive way. Here are the words that she carried over from her native Ireland. They may be recorded nowhere else. My father had a friend, Jimmy Grogan, who was a good Irish tenor. He would come to our house of a summer's evening. We would gather around the old Baldwin piano. My sister Mary, or my father, would play and Jimmy would sing all the old Irish "come-all-ye", as Nana used to call them. She would sit in a corner chair and listen, make requests, and occasionally join in. Her favorite was "Mary, The Rose of Tralee." I think there was a personal connection there from her own past, and she misted up each time she heard it sung.

She had so many stories to tell. Some were from her own experience and original to her. Others she had heard from other storytellers over the years. Someone once said that whoever tells a story the best owns it, and to that extent she owned all her own stories. One of her favorites was about Tim Nolan and the Pastor's Coat. Tim was a good man, and a singer too, but he was overly attracted to strong drink. Too much of his time and too much of his meager wages were lost at the local tavern after work. His wife, Nora, went to see Father Maxwell and asked for his counsel and advice with the problem. Father Maxwell came up with a plan.

He knew that Tim did not own a winter coat and needed one desperately. Father Maxwell had one perfectly good coat and his family had given him another the previous Christmas. No one needs two winter coats, so he decided to use one of them to solve Tim's problems. He called Tim into the rectory and told him that he was about to be gifted with a warm, black coat that had belonged to the pastor himself. Tim, good Catholic that he was, was both pleased and honored.

"You know, Tim," the good priest said, imbedding the hook gently, "it would not be right to wear a priest's coat in that tavern, nor to wear it while under the influence of drink."

"It would be sacrilegious," Tim agreed, "no man could do it." Father Maxwell was well pleased. "Here then is my coat," he said, passing it on to Tim for warmth and solving the Nolan family problem all in one glorious transaction.

"And for the rest of that winter," Nana said, "we would watch Tim Nolan coming up the hill from the tavern. There he'd be in the shivering cold, with no coat to warm him, singing at the top of his lungs and drunk as a lord, but honoring his word, he carried Father Maxwell's coat folded neatly over his arm."

"And then there were the O'Mara's," she said. "They had the first automobile in the neighborhood after The Great War and were desperately proud of it. They used to drive slowly around at night with the inside lights on so the neighbors would be sure to know it was them."

And the Egan's were another story. "Mrs. Egan had too many daughters and too little patience. There were seven little girls in that house and they fought from the time they got up in the morning until the time they went to bed at night. The summers were worse. They were home all the time from school and the poor woman just couldn't stand it. We knew it was near summer's end when the back door would swing open and out would run all the girls with their mother right behind them, swinging the broom at them and yelling, "To the playground, rats!'

"I once sent your mother and May to invite the girls to go with them for a swim at the little beach on McTaggert's Pond. Mrs. Egan came to the door and said, 'No! My girls can't go swimming until they learn how.'" Nana liked that one.

Who could forget her stories of the Cassidy family? Mr. Cassidy had a large family and not much money—which he begrudged spending on anyone including himself. When a member of the family was sick and requested cough syrup or aspirin or such, Mr.

Cassidy would test their faith by saying, "Ye need none of that expensive medicine stuff when ye have your Catholic faith to sustain ye. I'll give you a couple of tablespoons of Holy Water and ye'll be fine by morning." Alas, it is not recorded how well the Cassidy Cure worked in practice.

Then there was Danny Mack, the village moneylender whom you'll meet in Nana's "Christmas Story." Danny was not a popular man in Nana's village. When he finally died, they brought old Tim into the wake to see the man he had hated for years finally in death. "You see, Tim," the priest said, "Danny is dead. The hatred should end here."

"All right," said old Tim grudgingly, "but I'd feel better if we put a stake through his heart." The great Irish joke at the time was, "There were only two people at the wake, and their job was to make sure he didn't leave."

Wakes and funerals were great social events to Nana, and we talked about more than one. She never quite recovered from the O'Malley funeral. Mrs. O'Malley, good woman that she was, died young and left a grieving husband and family. The Hibernian Band led the funeral procession to the cemetery and played appropriate music during the burial ceremony. Then, leaving the cemetery, with the widower in tow, they suddenly broke into an enthusiastic rendition of "The Girl I Left Behind." Nana managed to tell this one with a chuckle and a tear, both at the same time.

The Doyle family was a sad case. They had serious financial problems and were just getting by. Mr. Doyle had not worked in some time and the family was supported financially by the odd jobs the children did while the mother took in laundry. It was a bleak life. However, their Grandfather Doyle was a well-known local orator and poet. He held the family together. He had written a great epic poem that he recited on high holidays and such other times as were necessary to lift the family's spirits. He told them that one-day his great epic would be sold and would bring them all a great fortune. They believed, and kept on going because of it. Nana and my mother knew most of this lengthy work and between them could recite nearly the whole thing. They could even remember many of Grandfather Doyle's elegant Victorian gestures. It was wonderful to behold. I

8

wish I could do it today. For some reason, all I can remember of what they told me is the epic's plaintive conclusion:

Grandfather Doyle would collapse his arms before him in the best theatrical fashion, bow his head, and dramatically intone:

"The wind that blows, through the grass that grows, will n'eer come back again."

This may be the only place in the world where Grandfather Doyle's epic poem is remembered, let alone reproduced for the wonderment of all.

Then there was the story of our neighbor, Delia Murphy. After a long career as a wife and mother, and some twenty years as a widow spent working in the paper mills, Delia retired. She planned to take her bit of money and return to the Ireland she hadn't seen since girlhood for a family visit. And the folks back home were glad indeed to see her. They threw her the most magnificent party with all the relatives in attendance along with all the townspeople and most of their friends. It went on all day and night, there was music and storytelling, the food was in abundance and the porter flowed like water. When it finally ended, the family came to her with a little presentation. She opened it eagerly. It was the bill for the party.

There were stories from the old days in Ireland too. There was the one about the priest who had spoken too sharply against the British occupation troops. Everyone told him to be quiet, he was just courting trouble, but he couldn't do it. One Sunday morning he was found murdered outside his little church. The authorities said the Tinkers did it. Nobody believed that. No tinker would dare strike down a priest. No one else was ever charged.

The people struck back in little ways. Nana told of one old lady who was pushed down in the street by a couple of ruffian British soldiers. An officer happened by at just that moment and he chewed them out sharply for their misbehavior. He helped the old woman to her feet and apologized for the indignity she had suffered. "Thank you, sir," she said sweetly, "and if there is a cool spot in Hell, I hope you get it."

Then there was the tourist from Boston who went on a walking tour of the Irish countryside. He ended up in a little farm village and stopped to buy some bread rolls from the two sisters who ran the local bakery. "I don't recognize your accent, sir," said one of the sisters as she wrapped his rolls in paper. "What part of England are you from?"

"Not England at all," he said, "I'm from America, near Boston."

"You're an American?" she said with a warm smile, reopening the package of rolls she had just wrapped and putting them back on the tray. "Wait another moment, sir, and we'll give you some clean ones."

Once when she was talking to my brother Leo and sensed he was not paying attention, Nana told him about Margaret, the maid she worked with in Ireland.

Margaret and Nana as young women worked for the priests of Lixnaw as cooks and housekeepers. Margaret, Nana said, never did anything without being told several times. The priest would have to remind her to start dinner, sweep the floor, or serve tea. Margaret's answer was always the same: "I'm on my way to do that now, Father." She said this several times a day in response to whatever instruction he gave her. It annoyed him because he knew she wasn't listening.

One day as Margaret was moping about, the priest asked, "Margaret, have you washed my books yet?" "I'm on my way to do that now, Father," she said. The priest told her, "Don't do it then, Margaret. Sure, it would only ruin them anyway." It took Margaret a while to get the point. It took Leo a lot less time and he listened carefully when Nana spoke to him after that.

Her beloved Catholic Church was a frequent topic of her tales. She told the story of the man who robbed and murdered the village priest's brother. He then went to confession to this same priest and admitted his guilt. He knew that the priest could never share with anyone this horrible knowledge of his brother's death being bound, as he was, by the Seal of Confession. You shall see how justice unfolded in this little morality tale in one of the later chapters of this book.

As Nana grew older, she became the subject of as many family stories as she was the source. Nana was an original, and an authentic family and neighborhood character. My sister Mary's favorite memory was the "Story of the Papal Scroll."

When Mary became engaged to be married, her fiancé, Paul Morin, had an uncle who was a Catholic priest with ties to Rome and even into the Vatican itself. As a wedding present, Father Morin presented them with a Papal Scroll. This was a parchment blessing on their marriage signed by the Pope himself, Pope Pius XII. My mother told Nana of this great honor.

"Thanks be to God!" Nana said, raising her arms in prayer." What a wonderful gift it is. Now, what will they do with it?"

It was a strange question. "What will they do with it?" my mother echoed.

"Yes," said Nana, "they can't let it outside in the trees, can they?"

"Ma," said my mother, "what are we talking about?"

"Why, about the squirrel, of course," said Nana. "The holy squirrel that was blessed by the Pope himself!"

A personal favorite of mine had to do with the Easter Holy Water. Nana could not go to Church, so the Church came to her. Every first Friday of each month the priest came to give her Holy Communion and his blessing. First Fridays were an important Church tradition at that time. Simply put, Catholics believe that if you received Holy Communion on the First Friday of each month for nine consecutive months, you were guaranteed the ministrations of a priest before death. That meant you died in the State of Grace, and that meant immediate entrance into Heaven. It was like a first class, guaranteed reservation to the next life.

Nana took no chances. If nine First Fridays were good, she figured, than ninety First Fridays would be even better. She had been on the First Friday schedule for as long as any of us could remember.

One First Friday, just after Easter, the priest came to visit our house with Holy Communion for Nana. He brought her a special gift: A small bottle of the special Holy Water that was blessed as part of the annual Easter Saturday Service. You made the Sign of the Cross with it on your forehead and received a special Easter blessing. He put the little bottle in her hand after Communion and said, "It's the

Easter Water, Mrs. Ware. I brought you a little bottle of Easter Water."

I don't know what Nana thought he said. She took the bottle from his hand and opened it. Then, with a neat little toasting gesture, she tipped it up on her head and drank the whole thing down in one gulp. My mother was shocked, while the priest looked on in amusement. Mother started to apologize but the priest just smiled and patted her hand. "That's all right, Dear," he said, looking affectionately at Nana. "Her insides will be good now until next Easter."

And speaking of the Faith, one night, Fr. Friel, a friend of my father's from Sacred Heart Church, stopped by the house one October evening, as he often did, to have a drink and play Cribbage with Dad. I sat in, as I often did, to listen. I had already learned one of the Great Truths of Childhood: If you sit very quietly around grown-ups and pretend to be busy, reading a book for example, they often forget you are there. It worked this night too.

As the evening wore on, Fr. Friel told a story he had heard from a fellow priest at a retreat. It was about a man who had a dog for a valet. It sounded reasonable at the time. The hour was late and it was dark and quiet save for the ticking of the mantle clock and the priest's soft but dramatic voice. As he spun his story, it turned out that this dog, which could brush and press his master's suit, clean house, and prepare a meal—was in reality a demon from Hell. The fiend had cast himself in the role of a useful family animal to gain admission to a Catholic household. His plan was to tempt the family members one by one into grave sin, and end up dragging the lot of them into Hell for all eternity. Fortunately, the hound was recognized as the fiend he was by a vigilant parish priest who doused him with Holy Water. Whereupon, there was a clap of thunder, a cloud of black smoke, an acrid smell, and the devil dog was blasted back into the depths of Hell where he belonged.

I don't know why my father let me hear that story. Maybe he forgot I was there. I guess we got into it before he knew which way the priest was headed and - well, how bad can a priest's story be? It was pretty bad. I was terrified. I crept into Nana's room and found her dozing in her chair. I woke her up and told her the story as best I could recall it. She was more frightened than I was. Particularly since it came from the priest who, in her view, was quite close to the Pope himself in the infallibility department. I didn't want to go upstairs alone any more than she wanted to stay downstairs alone. I fell asleep with her. My father moved me to my own bed later in the night. I never heard that particular story told back to me in any way at any time thereafter. I also noticed the frequency of her saying the rosary increased dramatically over the next several days.

My mother told of mysterious little things that seemed to happen around Nana. In the early 1930's, for example, she asked my father, an amateur photographer, to take a picture of Nana Ware. Nana was glad of it and put on her finest outfit to sit for this photograph in our living room. There were no home flashbulbs in those days, so my father took a time exposure. He set the camera on a tripod and opened the lens. Nana had to sit perfectly still in her chair for some ninety seconds to let the image register on the film. Any movement at all would cause a blur in the finished picture. The lens was opened and the countdown began. My mother and father were talking about something, paying little attention to Nana, until they noticed she was gone. "Ma!" my mother cried. "I'm right here," Nana said, coming back from the kitchen leaning heavily on her cane. "I just went into the kitchen for a drink of water." Later, when my father got the printed picture back from the studio, he couldn't explain it. There was no blur at all. It was the best picture of Nana we have.

Brother George told how his job was to leave Nana a drink each night when he came in from work. Usually it was water, or maybe juice. He left it in a little glass on her bureau so she could find it if she got up during the night.

It seems Nana had seen the doctor and complained that her energy level was too low. She asked him to give her something for the condition. The doctor was wise enough not to suggest it might have something to do with her being in her nineties. He suggested a glass of wine at bedtime might help. Nana liked that suggestion and asked George to leave her a glass of wine on her bureau as he went to bed.

One night, George couldn't find a wine glass or was in a hurry, so he left the open wine bottle itself on her bureau. Off he went to bed. Everything was fine until the next morning when he awakened to a crash at six o'clock. Thinking Nana had fallen, he rushed down to her room and found her singing a happy tune as she pulled all the covers off the bed and tried to turn the mattress herself. "Nana, what are you doing?" he asked. "I'm all right, dear," she said, "just changing the bed and turning the mattress. It's wanted doing for some days now and I figured this was a good time to get it all done."

"At six o'clock in the morning?"

"It is?" she asked. Just then, the empty wine bottle rolled out from under the bed. It was clear that Nana's energy level had been restored. George helped her tidy up and got her back into her bed where she fell into a deep and peaceful sleep. My mother shook her finger at him when she heard the story. "Just a glass! Never again the whole bottle."

That was the only story I have about Nana and strong drink. It just wasn't something she cared that much about. Once in a while, she did talk about potteen, the local home brew of Ireland. It was made from potatoes and was "So strong it can make a cat talk and a man dumb." I later learned that when the Irish clergy came out against potteen, they said that distilling it was a sin so serious, it could only be forgiven by a bishop. The rule was soon changed out of respect for the bishops' time. They just couldn't keep us with the demand to forgive this particular sin.

Nana ate dillisk, another item not to be found on your local grocer's shelves. It is a form of red seaweed, rich in salt, iron, and iodine, - and dismal in flavor. It tastes like the dry, salty weed that it is, but is supposedly good for you. I suppose anything that bad has to be good for you. Dillisk is very old. The Norsemen mention it in the Icelandic Sagas written of their raids on Ireland over one thousand years ago. Nana's parents ate it as part of their regular fare during the Great Famine. By Nana's time, dillisk was considered a health supplement. In the 1940's, Nana ate dillisk as a special snack, and perhaps a reminder of home. I always managed to decline when someone gave her a small supply of dillisk and, as ever, she was anxious to share.

She was never critical or judgmental about her family. She accepted people the way they were, and had a good word to say about everybody. There was no bitterness. I do remember as I grew older and said something that was particularly naive (or foolish) she might say, "God keep ye simple, child." I soon learned that when I heard that expression it was time to re-examine whatever it was that I had just said or done to warrant this considered observation.

To Nana, everything was new. Everything was an adventure. When she would go for a ride in the family car I would sit by her side and tell her how quickly we were traveling over the road to town she had walked so many times in her younger days. Now we are at the bridge. Now we are on Kimball Street. No matter how many times I told her, she always marveled at the speed of our movement. She would clasp my hand and say, "Surely, we aren't there already?" It was a delight to travel with her and be her faithful guide.

There are so many of her insights and expressions with me today. I remember in grammar school when the Church changed the rules regarding Holy Communion. Previously, you could not partake of Communion unless you had abstained from all food and beverages, including water, from the previous midnight. This was a terrible hardship, particularly for the elderly. Eventually the Church relaxed the rule. Now you could take water up until two hours before receiving Holy Communion. The nun who taught my religion class thought this was the personification of weakness. Although she dared not criticize Rome, she did tell us that we should observe the old rule anyway. It was the right thing to do. I was confused about that, and told Nana what had happened and asked her opinion. She replied simply, "Ye need not be holier than the Pope." I understood exactly what she meant. I have used that expression many times since to help find my balance between authority and opinion.

Nana's life was dedicated to her faith, but she thought for herself too. Many of the stories I brought home from the nuns at St. John's Grammar School reflected their personal vows of poverty, chastity, and obedience more than they did the realities of how people thought and felt and needed to act in the real world. There was a story I told her once, about an Irish saint—St. Cummins was his name. A lovely young princess and her royal prince came to him once to pledge their love to each other and become married before God and man. St. Cummins told them they had a special opportunity

15

to pledge their love to the Lord instead. They could guarantee their thrones in heaven by promising never to see each other again. He advised them to live as pilgrim spirits, alone in the world, apart from the one they loved. The couple agreed to this major modification of their wedding plan and lived long and lonely lives, forever in each other's heart but never in each other's arms.

"St. Cummins did that?" Nana asked incredulously.

"He did."

"Humph," said Nana, "he had little to do."

Nana's world was filled with little pleasures. When I got a part-time job in high school I bought her a forty-nine cent Easter orchid in a small glass vial filled with water. Her eyes misted over as she smiled and said, "This is my first corsage."

She stayed in continuing touch with her children and grandchildren. They visited her frequently and kept her apprised of their lives and careers - and yes, more family gossip. You never kept a story from Nana. Somehow, she could sense when something wasn't being said, and she would pry the details out of you as surely as would the most experienced interrogator.

She was an unusual woman. She was tough, loving, funny, and upbeat. She was a product of the 19th century living smack dab in the middle of the bustling 20th century. She loved to tell stories. She said "ye" instead of "you," and "tay" instead of "tea." I thought that was pretty funny at the time. I thought it was like speaking to someone from another time and another world. Now I know that is exactly what it was. Her stories remind me of an old Irish poem I read many years ago. The last line of it sounds like Nana's personal credo: "Come sing and dance with me in Ireland."

This recollection is all about her and her stories. I begin each one by setting the stage with a memory of my own from our family lives and adventures in the 1940's. Whatever adventure we had led to one of Nana's tales as surely as all the roads in Italy lead to Rome.

They say you are alive as long as people talk lovingly about you. I hope these stories will keep Nana alive well into the new century.

The Songs

Before I tell you about the songs that Nana Ware sang as she went about her daily activities, I would like to tell you about Tim Nolan, a friend of our family and a local singer of some modest repute. As my mother would say of Tim's singing by way of praise, "He was sincere and enthusiastic, and sang loud enough to be heard by all." Once again the women in my family demonstrated that you can say something nice about anybody if only you try. Here is Tim Nolan's story:

Christmas 1947: Tim Nolan At The Hannah Rest Home

Tim Nolan sang the Irish songs, to make the hearts feel glad,
He sang of wars so happy and of love affairs so sad.
He sang these plaintive ballads in his simple Irish way,
And in his mind he sounded very much like Dennis Day.

Now, the Irish love their tenors—just as everybody should,
But the problem with Tim Nolan was, he wasn't very good.
He would sing at wakes and weddings and beneath the Christmas wreath,
But when he hit the high notes, all the neighbors ground their teeth.

Well, at Christmas, '47, Tim—our grinning, Gaelic gnome,
Put in a guest appearance at the Hannah nursing home.

He sang the songs of Christmas, and the homeland tunes so sad,
And everyone who heard him swears, he sounded dreadful bad.

His voice cracked on the high notes, and it broke upon the low,
And the old folks prayed in silence that he'd pack it in and go.
They didn't clap, they didn't tap, they didn't sing along,
For fear this would encourage him to sing another song.

So he finished with "Oh Mother Mine, From Erin's Isle So Fair,"
And then gave his blessing to the old folks that were there:
"And may the wind be on your back, and may your dreams come true.
And may you all get better,"
And the old folks said, "You too!"

Now, these are the songs Nana sung as she went about her life
in the house on Temple Street. They were never written down until
now. I remember them because I heard them so often as I sat with her
and did my homework, or just happened to be in the general vicinity
as she sang them to herself for the comfort and company of her own
voice. I checked in old music and bookstores, including those that
specialize in Irish music, and never found any record of these songs. I
asked singers of Irish songs for information—but to no avail.
Recently, I showed the songs to John Kiley, an old friend and a bit of
a musical history buff. John found interesting references to two of the
songs in some UK archives. His comments are shown along with the
words of the respective songs. I think I alone may know the tunes to
these songs. Invite me to your next party and I'll sing them for you.
The songs are certainly close enough to indicate a common root.
Nana's versions, however, still stand as my original. I believe she
brought them with her from her own 19th century Ireland, the land "of
sad loves and happy wars," as my mother used to say. The songs
touch us from that distance even today:

Barney Mavourneen*

*"Mavourneen" is Gaelic for "Beloved."

This little song tells an idealized tale of love and respect triumphing over compromise and earthly desires. This is not a theme overemphasized in contemporary popular music.

'Twas a cold winter's night and the tempest was snarling.
The snow, like a sheet, covered cabin and sty.
When Barney flew over the hills to his darling,
And rapped at the window where Kitty did lie.
"Ara, Kitty," said he, "are you waking or sleeping?
'Tis a cold winter's night and my coat it is thin.
The storm is a brewing; the frost is a making,
And Kitty Mavourneen, won't you let me in?"

"Ara, Barney," said Kate, as she spoke through the window.
"How could you be taking me out of my bed?
To come at this hour 'tis a shame and a sin too.
It's whiskey, not love, has got into your head.

"If you really loved me of my fame you'd be tender.
Consider the hour, there is nobody in.
With what but her name can a poor girl defend her?
And Barney Mavourneen I won't let you in."

"Ara, Kitty," said he, "mine eyes are a fountain,
Which weep at the wrong I might lay at your door.
Your name is far whiter than snow on the mountains.
And your Barney would die to preserve it as pure.

"So I'm off to my home though the winter winds face me,
And I'll whistle them off, for I'm happy within.
And the voice of my Kitty shall comfort and bless me:
'And Barney Mavourneen, I won't let you in.'"

Erin Go Bragh*

*"Erin Go Bragh" is Gaelic for "Ireland Forever."

This is one of the songs friend John Kiley found mentioned in the UK archives. He reports it as a Scottish song. Nana's version has all the Scottish bits carved away and it has become a completely Irish experience. I guess whoever keeps the songs alive, like those who write history, gets to tell it their way.

Just for comparison, here's the first verse of the Scottish tune:
"My name's Duncan Campbell from the shire of Argyll,
I've traveled this country for many the mile.
I've traveled through Ireland, Scotland and a',
And the name I go under's bold Erin Go Bragh."

And now, Nana's version of Erin Go Bragh::

My name is Pat Gannon, perhaps you have heard,
I've toured all this country afar,
Through England, through Ireland, and the islands at large,
And the name that I go by is Erin Go Bragh.

Once on my encounters through Liverpool's streets,
A saucy policeman I chanced for to meet,
He looked in my eye and he gave me some jar,
Saying, "What brought you over from Erin Go Bragh?"

"I know you're a Pat by the coat that you wear.
I see you're a Pat by the cut of your hair."
"Indeed I'm a Pat, and that's very true,
But if I were an eagle, pray what's that to you?"

A stick of black thorn I had clenched in my fist,
And around his broad shoulders I soon did it twist.
The blood from his napper I quickly did draw.
And I showed him the games played by Erin Go Bragh.

The people were round me like flocks of wild geese,
Shouting, "Rest Irish Pat 'fore he kills the police!"
For beating the Bobbies and breaking the law,
Six months at hard labor for Erin Go Bragh.

Oh, Pat had the fight,
But they had the law,
And six months at hard labor,
Was Erin Go Bragh.

The Shepherd's Daughter

This song shows the woman as anything but the passive victim of an advantage-taker. This young woman, who seemingly has no recourse against her noble lover, goes right to the top: She visits the King himself and convinces him to right the wrong that has been committed against her. Then as now, if the King's on your side, you'll probably be treated fairly.

This song is perhaps the most interesting song in the Nana collection. John Kiley found this one too in the UK archives (http://www.contemplator.com/folk3/knight.html). It is entitled "The Knight and the Shepherd's Daughter." The song was popular during the time of Queen Elizabeth I, and was printed during her reign with her picture on it. It also appeared in a comedy called "The Pilgrim"—which was published in 1621. It too has been brought more into an Irish vernacular. I don't know if Nana did that herself, but it does amaze me that our family has shared a role in keeping this story alive from sometime before 1621 until 2002 when these words are being written. Here's Nana's version:

With my bonnie bunch of flowers,
And my roses all in bloom,
And no more shall I go roving,
So late an afternoon.

There was a shepherd's daughter, kept watch upon a hill,
And there a lordly gentleman rode by her at will,

With my bonnie bunch of flowers (etc.)

She hitched up here petticoats and followed the horse's tracks,
She came to the royal palace and down came the King,

21

With my bonnie bunch of flowers (etc.)

"Gather round, my royal lords, and hearken unto me,
For when her little babe is born, shall I name him after thee?"

With my bonnie bunch of flowers (etc.)

The King called down his merry men, by one, by two, by
three,
He called down his son William, the very man was he,

With my bonnie bunch of flowers (etc.)

William reached into his cloak, and he threw her his purse,
"And when your babe is born," said he, "let that be his nurse."

With my bonnie bunch of flowers (etc.)
"Oh, I'll not have your gold, fair sir, and I'll not take your fee,
But I'll have your own sweet body, which the King has given
to me,"

With my bonnie bunch of flowers,
And my roses all in bloom,
And no more shall I go roving,
So late an afternoon.

Fragments
They Say You've Left The Old Home, Jim

This sentimental piece has a haunting tune. I don't remember
all the words, but the gist of it is that Jim is leaving the village to seek
his fortune in the city. He goes to tell the young woman who loves
him of his decision. Before he can speak, she sings,

"They say you've left the old folks, Jim, they say you're
going away.

Away to all the cities bright and gay.
The old place won't be the same, Jim.
And the birds won't sing as sweetly when you're gone.
If you ever get in trouble, Jim, just write and let us know."
She said these words and then she turned away.

(Jim goes off to the city and earns his fortune, but at great price to his happiness and serenity. He works and lives alone for many years, thinking of who and what he left behind. The last verse goes:)

Oh and twenty years thereafter, there came a stranger to the village…

(He finds the young woman he left behind, still single and now alone like him. He asks her to marry him. She asks why now? He tells her she has never been out of his mind, and that every day he has heard her song:)

"They say you've left the old folks, Jim, they say you're going away.
Away to all the cities bright and gay.
The old place won't be the same, Jim.
And the birds won't sing as sweetly when you're gone.
If you ever get in trouble, Jim, just write and let us know."
She said these words, and then she turned away

And Ireland Will be Free

Nana sang this one as she puttered around her room. I gather it was a song the Irish sang in the 1800's to commemorate an abortive attempt by the French to help free Ireland. I remember just a few lines:

"'The French are in the bay, and help is on the way,' said the Seanchai"

The "Seanachai" (pronounced "shan-a-chee") was the revered historian and storyteller whom the people looked to for guidance under difficult circumstances. The Seanachai, and they might be either male or female, could tell them what happened in the past that they might use history as a guide to resolve their present difficulty. In this case, France, the historic enemy of England, was promising a French invasion to dispel the English occupiers. The French were Catholic, like the Irish, so the threatened invasion was welcome. The Irish saw the French as a gentler race than the formidable English and were ready to co-operate and support them. In return, the French promised to be a kinder and gentler occupier. As an unknown writer remarked at the time, "The Irish will resist chains of iron, but they can be led by a kindly hand holding a silken thread."

The song went on: "Will Ireland then be free?" said the Seanchai.

'Oh Ireland will be free from the center to the sea, and hurrah for liberty,' said the Seanchai."

I looked the matter up in Irish history. As usual, Nana had her story straight. In 1796, just two years before the 1798 Wexford uprising that cost so many lives, a French fleet sailed into Ireland's Bantry Bay, County Cork, with an army on board to expel their archrival England from Ireland. It looked like a good plan and the people rose up in rebellion counting on support from the French troops in the bay. Alas for them, high winds came up in the bay and blew non-stop for several days. The ships could not unload their troops and found it increasingly difficult even to hold their positions at anchor. Eventually, they had to sail back to France without contributing a single soldier to the uprising. The English troops who were quartered in Ireland moved against the rebels and ruthlessly crushed them. It was one more attempt at freedom, and one more major tragedy and disappointment.

However, Nana's song checked out as accurate on all its particulars.

1945: Nana and the Miracle

Many years ago, at St. John's Grammar School in West Fitchburg, I read Edgar Lee Masters epic, *Spoon River Anthology*. It is a collection of 250 little story poems, each about the life and times of one person from Masters' hometown of Spoon River. The people are good and bad, smart and stupid, honest and crooked—in short, just like people everywhere. The person whose life is depicted delivers their own autobiographical story poem from the Spoon River Cemetery on the outskirts of town. They are all dead and buried, but in this last moment they get to tell us about their lives, engage in a little self-justification, and say how they would like to be remembered.

I decided to write my own version of this masterpiece about the people and events surrounding me as I grew up in 1940's West Fitchburg. Naturally, the first story I wrote was about Nana Dunne Ware. This tale of Cousin Jim and his double-taped carton was one of my father's favorite stories. He was my source and I'm sure he amplified it for dramatic and comedic effect. My father firmly believed that an enhanced funny story is far better than a boring literal recitation of fact. I wonder where that gene ended up in my generation. Everyone in the family agrees that the story is mostly based on truth. I was only about 8 years old when it happened, but I still remember, or think I remember, the excitement and hubbub surrounding Nana's Miracle.

Nana and the Miracle

She was, the neighborhood all said, a living Irish saint,
Though she led a life that could have been the subject of complaint,
Just a wrinkled, wizened woman with the weight of many years,
Who had lots of time for love and prayer, but little time for tears.

She was Mary Dunne of Ireland, born in 1859,
And at 20 came here steerage, on the Cunard White Star Line.
She found a job and married, life was happy if a grind,
But at 40 she was widowed, and at 50 she was blind.

She worked to raise her family, and all of them helped out,
With far too much to do for much self-pity, or for doubt,
And then they were all grown and gone, that job was done and thus,
She was my mother's mother, so she came to live with us.

She was crippled with arthritis and her hearing was just fair,
She had her room and radio, and hardly left her chair,
Her person hardly left, that is, her mind was never still,
For the weakness of the body never spread into the will.

And Oh! The tales that she could tell to charm a little boy,
Of heroes, and of banshees, and the simple, country joy.
Her mother caught a leprechaun, and stared him in the eye,
But he grabbed his purse and disappeared and—would her mother
lie?

She saw Fitchburg's first electric light, the kids climbed up the
stands,
And when the squire turned it on, they screamed and clapped their
hands.
And sometimes, there were rebel tales, of how the hate began,
And the foreign occupation troops, who wore the Black and Tan.

She talked and she told stories, and she sang the songs of home,
Of people who would be as one, no matter where they'd roam.

26

There are many tales to tell of her, and what she said and did.
This first one's of my cousin, and the carton that he hid.

When Cousin Jimmy came to town, his mood was always bright.
He'd laugh and slip us money, and we knew that he was right.
His clothes were always perfect, and he talked a lyric brogue.
My father said he was a textbook charming, Irish rogue.

One night he came to see us, and the charm had turned to gloom.
He said there was "a problem," and they made us leave the room.
"Just a small misunderstanding," I later learned he said.
It seems a business friend of Jim's had got it in his head,
That Jim was holding out on him, it had to do with money.
"Except for the embarrassment, the whole thing would be funny.
"In any case, he's quite the snoop, and likes to poke around,
"And I don't want my private things left where they could be found."

"And so, I filled this carton with those few things all my own,
"And I ask for you to take it now, and keep it in your home."
You can't turn down a cousin, who is in a little scrape,
Even cousins with a carton that is double-sealed with tape.

My father simply took the box, and put it in the cellar,
Beneath the winter coats and boots, and Grandpa's old umbrella.
So out of sight and out of mind, this unknown cartonned thing,
Sat undisturbed through winter, and the early days of spring,

Sat undisturbed through winter storms, and early April airs,
While Nana went about her life, and prayed her special prayers.
For Nana had a lot of things, and gave the Lord her thanks,
But she didn't have the long, green stuff that people keep in banks.

She didn't lack for anything, in any form or measure,
But she wanted to leave kids like me, a legacy to treasure.
And so she prayed to Mary, let her know how much she'd thank her,
If God's own Blessed Mother sent a vision to some banker.

But April means—it's baseball time! And brother George's club,
Had scheduled on the schoolhouse flat, a pick-up game of scrub.
It was his year, he'd made the team, and baseball was his love,
But all the guys were waiting, and he couldn't find his glove.

It wasn't here, it wasn't there, he looked the house through twice,
And then he went to Nana, and she offered her advice.
She made him search his room again, and look in every closet,
(When George would put his things away, who knows where he'd
deposit?)

And so, he searched his room again, the attic and the cellar,
Beneath the winter coats and boots, and Grandpa's old umbrella.
And there he found a carton, underneath a dusty drape.
A carton without markings, double sealed with heavy tape.

He gave it just as much a though as any anxious kid,
And then took out his Boy Scout knife, and cut apart the lid.
The box was full of money! Each in neat and numbered band.
He dumped it out and counted it, it came to fifty grand.

Fifty thousand dollars—back in 1945!
He ran and told his Nana, and she cried, "Great God Alive!
"He has smiled on us, His people, on this best of all our days.
"Who knows, or understands, the working of His Holy Ways!"

"Now run and call your father, boy, and tell him of your find.
"While I say a Novena, that will help me to unwind."
And George did as his Nana said, and called his father's store,
And told him of the carton found upon the cellar floor.

He told him how he opened it, and found the fifty grand.
How Nana had the Miracle for which she'd prayed and planned.
Maybe we could travel (George would, of course, play hooky,)
But my father said, "Forget it! Cousin Jimmy is a bookie."

"I'm coming home to sort this out; it's not a gift from Heaven,

28

"It's more to do with horses, dogs, and seven-come-eleven."
So home he came, and took the box, and counted all the money.
He told Nana what had happened, and she didn't find it funny.

He placed a call to Cousin Jim, and made a choice remark,
And said to come and get the box, as soon as it got dark.
He swore us all to secrecy, and pulled the curtains wide,
Then sat there with the carton and a shotgun by his side.

When it grew dark, we watched a Packard Eight pull in the yard,
And the man with Cousin Jimmy looked unfriendly, cold and hard.
They counted it, re-taped the box, and put it in a sack,
And quickly drove away again, not ever looking back.

I never did see Jim again, that charming Irish fox.
And Nana mentioned it just once, in later private talks.
"At least no one is poorer, and nobody got hurt."
But little things like that, I thought, sure keep a kid alert.

So Nana said her Rosaries, and prayers of every shape,
And hoped to find another carton, double-sealed with tape.
And though that never happened, she succeeded beyond measure,
In leaving little kids like me, a legacy to treasure.

Nana And The Leprechaun

Nana Dunne Ware was my mother's mother. She came to live with us when we moved into the white house on Temple Street in 1939. My father's people had built the house some 30 years before and since he was sole surviving heir, the house and everything in it came to him. It was a comfortable eight room, white cape with black trim, and easily accommodated our extended family of seven people, plus an Irish Setter named Penelope (or Penny, as she preferred to be called). The human part of the family included Leo, Sr., my father, Kathryn Rose Rita, my mother, sister Mary, brothers Leo and George, and me, Edward - the youngest. There was another brother, Paul David, born two years before me. He died a few days after birth. Nana told me that my mother believed a careless nurse had dropped the baby in the Lucy Helen Hospital. The body was bruised was she saw it. When my mother asked what happened, the baby was taken away and she was not allowed to see it again. If it was a hospital cover-up, the mid 1930's was a good time for such things to happen and be hushed up.

In 1939, when Nana came to live in the downstairs corner room on Temple Street, I was 2 years old and Nana Ware was 80 years old. We became the best of friends.

Nana had worked hard all her life. In 1883, she came over from the village of Lixnaw in Ireland where she had been a maid for the parish priest, Father Kavanaugh. She came because her father, Michael Dunne, made a request of her on his deathbed. "There is nothing here for you, child," he told her. "Write my brother, your Uncle Timothy in America, for the travel loan. Then promise me you will go there and make a new life."

She stayed with her father until he died, and then did as he had asked. She was just over 20 years of age, alone, and this was her first trip outside her village. Her father's brother, Uncle Timothy, who lived in Fitchburg and had a crippled child, paid for her $30.00 ticket. Nana's job was to care for the child until the cost of the ticket was repaid. She bathed the child, dressed him, fed him, and carried him around on her back. It took two years to repay the loan.

In 1885 she married another immigrant Irishman, George H. Ware who coincidentally came from Lixnaw as well. He was a teamster for a wealthy farmer named William Fuller who competed in horse shows and exhibitions throughout the county. "Your grandfather could turn one of those horse teams and rigs around in less than their own length," she told me. They raised a large family, seven of whom survived into my era. By the time we met, Nana was a widow, blind, nearly crippled by arthritis, and anxious to contribute her share to the new household. She became my sitter, companion, advisor, entertainer, and friend.

Nana was a storyteller. The Irish call them Seanchai. Nearly everything that happened in our lives reminded her of a story. A few were dark, others were sad, most were funny, and all of them were entertaining. She kept us on the edge of our chairs. It was a rare story that didn't have some sort of message to think about later. I have read that the myths and stories of the Irish storytellers are history in disguise. The trick is to figure out which part is history and which part is disguise. One storyteller had a stock answer to the question, "Is that story true?" He would smile and respond, "Well, if it isn't, it should be." I think Nana's stories are often that way.

My favorite story was the one Nana told about her mother, Mary Kate Davis, and the Leprechaun she almost caught. It happened just this way:

Mary Kate and The Leprechaun

"When my mother, Mary Kate Davis, was a little girl - around 1826 or so - she lived near the Kerry woodlands, on the high road from Tralee to Tarbert. This was the countryside where the Leprechauns worked and played.

The Leprechauns were fairies and creatures to be contended with if you lived in rural Ireland. They were not malicious but they were mischievous and could cause a bit of trouble if they chose to. No one really knows why they disliked or maybe just feared people, but they did. Some said they were bitter because of an old curse that excluded them from Heaven. Without the hope of salvation it didn't matter to them if they were a little better or a little worse than anyone else. They often chose to be worse. This is what can happen if you're a little too bad for heaven, and a little too good for hell.

Others said they were fallen angels. The Leprechauns were the original followers of the brilliant archangel Lucifer, "the light bearer." To their eternal regret, they were more involved in his awesome company, sparkling conversation, and spellbinding story telling than they were in realizing that he was on the verge of refusing to serve God. The Seanchai said that when Lucifer heard that God would one day take human form and become man, his pride would not allow him to bend before a mere mortal. He said, "I will not serve." With those words his fate was sealed for all eternity. He was cast out of Heaven into the pits of Hell, and his admirers, the Leprechauns, were cast out with him. But, since their sin was much less than Lucifer's, so was their punishment. They were condemned to eternal life on earth as the sad, magical little creatures, neither human nor inhuman, we know as Leprechauns.

Most of the time, The Little People, as we called them, played harmless and irritating pranks. Have ye never set something down, turned away for a moment, and when ye came back to claim it again, found it gone? That's the Little People teasing ye. Ye must go out of the room and give them a chance to have their joke and put it back again. When ye return, there it is right where ye left it in the first place.

Then and now, there were ancient mounds all over rural Ireland. The people called them forts. These mounds were built over underground dwellings from distant times past. Some said they were prehistoric homes going back thousands of years to the Iron Age. Others said the fairies built them and it was best to keep entirely away from them. They were magic places. I remember one time when my father and his friends burned all the brush and grass surrounding one of the mounds to bring it out into the light. Next day, when they went back to check, there was no sign of the fire. The brush was as thick and the shade as dark as it had ever been.

My mother, Mary Kate, was often told by her parents to stay away from the mounds, and never go into the woods alone. There were unknown things there. But - this particular summer day was bright and warm and danger seemed a long way off. Mary Kate was looking for something a little interesting, if not exciting, to do. She was walking about in her own yard near the edge of the dark woods. It was then she heard the noise, coming from deep within the brush: "Tap, tap. Tap, tap, tap." She paused and listened. What was that?

"Tap, tap, tap." It came again, seemingly from a little meadow she knew existed somewhere inside those dark woods. What was that noise? Despite her mother's stern warning, and her father's threats, she decided to find out. Slowly, quietly, she entered the shadowed woodlands and headed toward the little meadow and the tapping sound.

"Tap, tap, tap." It was growing louder now as she approached the clearing. Gently, she pushed the brush aside and peered into the sunlit little meadow and looked about. She soon saw the cause of the tapping sound. It was a Leprechaun.

The little man was not a foot tall and he sat on a tiny stool, diligently repairing the little pairs of shoes that were neatly arranged on the ground around him. He was so intent on his work that he had no idea he had been heard, let alone found and observed, by this little girl who now watched him through the leaves and branches.

There's another thing ye must know about Leprechauns: They carry a magic purse. Every time ye open that purse, there is a shilling inside. How shall I tell ye what a shilling was worth at that time? Think of a week's wages for a man lucky enough to have a paying

job. That's a shilling's worth. Open the purse ten times and ye have
ten days wages. A hundred times means a hundred shillings. Why,
the old people said that if ye sat there all day just opening and closing
that little purse and claiming your prize each time, ye could live like
Queen Victoria herself for the rest of your life.

Mary Kate wanted that magical purse. She knew the rules
about how she could make it her own. Simply put, you had to sneak
up behind the Leprechaun and grab him around the waist before he
could disappear in a puff of smoke. The trick was to hang on,
regardless of what he said or did, until the purse was firmly in your
own fist. Only then could you let him go. Nothing else would work.

Now, sneaking up on a Leprechaun is like sneaking up on a
squirrel or a bird. It cannot easily be done. But - the best things in
life are never easily done. Besides, this Leprechaun was so old and
tired looking, and so intent on his work that Mary Kate decided to
give it a try.

Slowly, quietly, in stocking feet she made her way out of the
shrubbery and into the sun drenched meadow. Closer and closer she
came, stealing up behind him while his tapping and intense
concentration blocked out any notice of her approach. She moved
silently over the grass, closer and closer. Don't let him see the
shadow stealing toward him, and then…she grabbed him!

She had him! She had him! Fair and square she had him as
they bounced around the little clearing in the woods. "What is this,
then?" he cried. "Let me go! Let me go! I'm an old man and I must
be after mending my shoes!"

"None of your tricks," said Mary Kate. "I caught ye fair and
square and it's your magic purse I'll be after. Ye must give me your
purse and then ye will be free to go."

"I have no magic purse." he spat, not sounding quite as feeble
as he did at first, "Now let me go. You're hurting me."

Mary Kate did not want to hurt the little man, so she relaxed
her grip a slight bit. "There," she said, "I will not hurt ye, but I won't
let ye go until ye give me the magic purse."

The Leprechaun struggled silently for a moment or two, and
then with a deep sigh he said, "All right then, ye win. I do have a
magic purse and it's hidden on me person. You have won it fair and

square as ye say, and I must give it to ye. Let me go now so I can have it out of my tunic."

And Mary Kate flushed with success and beaming with joy, let go of the Leprechaun.

"What I'll give ye," the little man laughed, "is me dust!" And with that - Poof! - He was gone. Mary Kate found herself alone in the sunlit little clearing. She turned around and around, this way and that, but there was no one to be seen. She thought she heard the laughter of little voices as they moved away and grew faint and fainter with the distance until they were gone.

"My mother never told her parents what happened that day," Nana said. "She knew how angry they would be after warning her not to go near the woods, let alone the Little People. Mary Kate learned there were good reasons for rules. She also learned not to be taken in by smooth talk and made-up stories. However, until she grew up and moved away from the little farm near the woods, she would sit out in the yard on a warm summer afternoon and listen for the tap, tap, tapping of the little shoemaker. And she would remember her great adventure and dream about a second chance at the Leprechaun's magic purse."

And now, you ask, after all these years do I believe Mary Kate's story was true? Well, I would never question anything Nana Ware told me. Nor would I question anything Mary Kate told her. So, I guess I believe.

In fact, sometimes on a warm summer's afternoon, if I'm out in my yard and I hear a woodpecker tapping in the brush, I smile and wonder if I would have fared any better against that clever little Leprechaun. Could I have won his magic purse and the money that appeared within it? Perhaps not.

Nana And The Banshee

Halloween was an important holiday in 1940's West Fitchburg. In fact, it was the highlight of our autumn social season. As the days grew short and the winds grew cold, our thoughts would turn toward October 31st and the preparations for this High Holy Day among children would begin.

Nana said that Halloween came from Ireland with the Irish immigrants in the 1800's. It was a somber time and a scary night in the village of Lixnaw when she was a little girl. "The Seanchai said that when the old ones came to Ireland, thousands of years before, they started the custom of burying their dead in the mounds that dotted the countryside. They believed that on October 31, the last day of their year, the dead rose up and wandered about looking for food and money to keep them secure over the coming year. The people would leave little offerings of food and treats outside their door to keep these spirits content. Often, the children would come and take these things away early the next morning. I suppose that's where ye got the trick or treat custom ye have here in America. It was the Irish, ye know, that brought Halloween to this country."

The Church would have had Halloween a somber time in the 1940's too. The nuns would tell us that October 31st was All Hallows Eve, the night before the holy day of All Saints. That was the day when we remembered all the saints in Heaven who hadn't been grand enough to warrant a special day of their own. It was a time for prayer, they said, and reflection upon those saints and our own deceased loved ones. It was not a time for revelry and misbehavior. We bought all that to some degree, but even the nuns couldn't change the fact that it was Halloween! The night of ghosts and goblins and costumes and parties. It was time to have fun.

We would save up to buy a papier-mâché Jack-O-Lantern that could be illuminated if you had a flashlight small enough to fit inside. I never knew anyone who did. Some kids put little votive candles inside and although they worked, they were so dangerous their mothers would put them out before they burned down the house. Noisemakers were big too. There was one you swung around by a wooden handle and it made a loud clacking sound like the boys would make by tying a clothespin onto the frame of their bikes and letting it clatter against the spokes.

The costumes were homemade, and more enthusiastic than creative. There were many ghosts in white sheets and pillowcases, and a few clowns in mismatched but colorful clothes and their mother's make-up. I was a soldier. I had an army pistol belt and canteen that Uncle George had worn in World War I, and a German helmet that my cousin Phil liberated from a supply depot in Italy during World War II. It all worked, I guess. No one really cared as long as you entered into the spirit of things, be it trick or treating or the parties.

There was always a Halloween party, and sometimes two. The mothers' guild at St. John's Grammar School sponsored a party for the whole neighborhood on Halloween. There was recorded music, like Bing Crosby's version of "Ichabod Crane," "Teddy Bear's Picnic," and "Little Sir Echo." There were games like dunking for apples, pin the tail on the donkey and throwing darts at water-filled balloons for little prizes. The highpoint of the evening came when the school sexton, Mr. Nicholas, came with a huge cloth moneybag that was filled with nickels. We took turns reaching into the bag and filling one fist with as many nickels as we could hold. The rules were simple: You could have all the nickels you could take out of the money bag and put into your own pocket - without spilling or dropping any. Whatever you dropped went back into the moneybag for the next person. "Mr. Nickels," as we called him this night, would shake his head at the greedy that tried to take too many, dropping

37

most of them on their way to a pocket. The secret was to go for only as many as your fist could close around. Better the few in your pocket than the many on the floor. As Nana would say when I told her what happened, "God helps the needy, not the greedy."

The other party was at Wes Withington's Antique Auction Barn. Wes was a good soul who operated an antique and used furniture business from a huge old car barn out behind his house. My mother bought an oak corner table there once for fifty cents. Everyone agreed that it was a good buy. In later years I wondered what he would have paid for an oak table to be able to sell it for fifty cents and still make a profit. I suspect it was not much.

Wes' party was always a success. First of all, the old barn filled with furniture and memories added to the Halloween mood and imparted a dark and spooky feeling to the festivities. Walking down a poorly lit back road to get there helped that feeling too. It was even gloomier coming home after the party. The older kids would leave first and then hide in the woods along the way, ready to jump out and scare us as we made our nervous way back home.

There were costumes, parties, trick-or-treating and then often we would end the evening with a story from Nana Ware.

We always went in to show her our costumes, never considering the fact that she was blind. She would feel every inch of the costume, pat us down, ask a few questions, and then guess what we were supposed to be. Since the costumes were all hand-me-downs from my older brothers Leo and George, and even my sister Mary, perhaps it wasn't as difficult a task as it seemed at the time. It was miraculous back then.

As the chatter and gossip died down, I would say, "Nana, tell us a story." And this is one of the stories that Nana told:

The Banshee of Lixnaw

"In the little village where I grew up in Ireland, Lixnaw was its name, in the parish of Finuge, the Banshee was respected by day and feared by night," she began. "The Banshee is a ghost. Not an evil one like ye have today in your books and movies, but perhaps a soul trapped between this world and the next and filled with sadness because it was part of neither. It had no kinship with either the living or the dead. It was alone in God's creation. The Banshee wanted rest and peace, but did not know how to achieve either. It was alone, sad, and confused. No one knows how the Banshee got into this terrible fix. The Seanchai, the storytellers, said it had to do with some unfinished business when they died. Their soul got off the track to Heaven to try and fix something, and didn't know how to get back on again. I guess this offended God. He let them wander around for a while as a punishment for not promptly heeding His call. They moaned and wailed the livelong night, sometimes for years and years, until God or St. Patrick took pity on them and put them once again on the road to Heaven. As I say, they were not evil, but ye stayed away from them entirely. An upset horse may not want to harm ye, but ye can get kicked or trampled just the same if ye come too close.

When I was a little girl, we had a Banshee in Lixnaw.

The Banshee lived outside of town, near a crossroads, by an old fort in the woods. I've told ye about the forts. They were the strange mounds that could be found all over rural Ireland - and they had been there before memory itself. Some thought they were the tombs of old kings and chieftains. Others say they went back thousands of years to when people lived underground for protection against nature and the elements. Some say they were home to the Little People.

We all knew enough to leave the forts alone. Oh, once in a great while some foolish person might dig into one to try and move it, or cultivate it, or just see what was inside. Whatever the reason, it was a bad thing to do. 'Disturb a fort,' my father would say, 'and ye will never have another day's good luck.'

The wailing and caterwauling of the Banshee of Lixnaw was causing considerable trouble in the village. It had started in the late summer and seemed to get worse as the autumn season came upon us. By late October it was very bad indeed. People were afraid to leave their homes after dark. Even the men who played darts and smoked and gossiped at Mallahy's Pub in the square would walk home together in two's and three's for comfort and protection. Some of the cows stopped giving milk, and the sheep that had been sheared in the spring were slower growing their coats than anyone could remember.

Constable Doyle still made his rounds each night, but he held the lantern high in front of him, and his other hand was never far from the truncheon he carried in his belt.

And from dusk until dawn, the Banshee howled.

All in all, it was a bad time in Lixnaw. My sisters Kate, Nell, and I never left my mother's side after dark. From the time we cleaned up and finished the evening chores, we sat with her by the turf fire in the stone fireplace my father had built. We would not venture outside again until the sun was high and the animals needed to be fed and cared for.

It was the parish priest, Father Kavanaugh, who finally decided it was time for action. When the women would not come out even for his Sunday night devotional, he knew that something had to be done. He called all the village men to a meeting in the little sitting room of the cottage he rented next door to the chapel. He left the windows open and told everyone to speak up so the men who had to stand outside could be part of the discussion.

'I'm not saying there is a Banshee, and I'm not saying there is not a Banshee,' the old priest said. 'There are things that exist outside of what we know and understand, and the Banshee could well be one of those things.'

The men liked that. They did not want to be told they were frightened by their imaginations or superstitions. The people of that time kept their feelings to themselves. However, they had grown up with stories of the Little People in the woodlands, and the forts in the dark woods, and the old ones who slept in the mountains. Even the parish priest himself, good man that he was, could not change any of that.

'So, here is what we do,' the priest continued. 'We go out there to the crossroads Sunday morning, after Mass. We go as a patrol; like in the army, don't you know. Then, we will split into four groups and each group will search a quadrant around that area as I have shown on this map. I will give each team chieftain a copy. We will look for anything unusual - forts, graves, construction, anything unusual, and anything out of the ordinary. Then we will meet back here for tea and discussion and agree upon what we will do next.'

40

It was a good plan and the men agreed to it. The next Sunday they all took Holy Communion and, after Mass, my father, Michael, was first outside the church to help form up the search parties. Fr. Kavanaugh appointed him one of the team leaders and gave him the map showing the wooded area near the crossroads where he and his men were to search. My mother gave him a blessed medal to wear as protection against the Banshee. My father himself brought along his shovel with the long stout handle as protection against anything else he might meet that would cause him trouble. The other men were similarly armed with shovels, hay rakes, and pitchforks. After a brief prayer, they set off on their walk to find the Banshee.

It was a good stretch of the legs to the crossroads, but they talked and smoked their white clay pipes. They kept each other company and the time passed quickly. In what seemed like short order, they were at the crossroads. They split into four groups as agreed, and my father and his six men set off in the direction toward the woods and the old forts.

They saw nothing unusual at first. The sun was bright and the day warm for this late in autumn. The birds sang sweetly and occasionally they scared up a small animal from the woodlands, and watched him scurry away to cover in the brush. 'Then, my father said, 'It started to go dark. Not with the end of day, mind you, but we were in the woods now and the branches overhead blocked out the sunshine. It grew cold and damp. There were no birds singing here. All grew quiet.'

'We are near the forts,' said one of the men.

He had no sooner said that then there it was before them: One of the magic mounds. It was very big indeed. A huge mound of earth piled higher than the tallest man and big enough to fill up the village square. It was covered with decaying brush and moss and dead grass and smelled damp and spoiled. It took some time for the group to make their way around it and take it all in.

'Someone's been digging here, Michael.'

They all looked toward where he pointed. There was a hole there, about the size of a small dog or cat, right into the side of the fort. My father knelt down and ran the handle of his shovel inside to see how deep it went. It took the entire length of the shovel and never encountered a single obstruction. 'It's not a hole, it's a tunnel,' he told them.

'That's how the Banshee got out' one man said.

'There's no dirt out here,' said another man. 'That means it was dug from the inside out.'

'It's the Little People,' said a third man, crossing himself.

'Whatever it is,' my father said, 'it's the source of the problem. We will get the others, and then fill it in. I think we should burn back this brush and growth and bring this thing out into the sun where God Himself can watch it.'

And that is just what they did. The men came and used their shovels to fill in the tunnel and then tamp it down. They pushed the dirt inside as far as the longest shovel or branch would allow them, and then packed it down until the ground where the tunnel had been was as tight and hard as the mound itself. Then they tore the brush away and lit a fire. They burned all the dead growth and branches that had kept the fort hidden away for so many years. By the end of their day's work the fort was whole once again, and standing out free and clear in the sunlight, away from the darkness that had covered it for so many years.

The men went home then. There was no talking and joking as there had been on the walk out. They were along with their thoughts. They had their suppers, and then sat up until dark to hear if the Banshee would cry that night. There was no cry or wail. The Banshee was silent that night, and the next, and the next. Life in the village returned to normal and people came out again after dark.

Fr. Kavanaugh said it must have been the wind that did it. Some small animals burrowed a hole in the mound and hit a hollow space where the wind would get trapped and howled like the Banshee we thought it was. It was one solution to the problem. My father, of course, saw it differently.

'What animal is it that burrows into the side of a hill? And where did he hide all the dirt?' he asked. 'And if it was the wind that was howling like the Banshee, why did it only howl at night and not by day? Something…was disturbed,' he told us knowingly. 'And that thing could not rest until it was once again sealed up from all interference from the outside world.'

That's almost the end of the story. Years later when I was near grown, I asked him about it again.

'Mary,' he said, 'there's one more thing I never told ye nor your mother, nor your sisters. The day after we filled in the tunnel and burned the brush, we went back out there again to make sure nothing had been disturbed. We found the fort and it was whole once again. Ye could not even find the place where the tunnel had been. But there was no sign of yesterday's fire. The fort was covered again with brush and dead grass and the branches grew over it shielding it from the sun just as it was the first time we saw it. The Banshee had put its house in order and was once again at rest within its fort.'

That was the final word. We never spoke of it again."

A Christmas Story

The Christmas holiday at home during the Forties looms very large in my memory. It was an old fashioned family Christmas with lights indoors and out, candles in the windows, trees and presents and excitement and the smell of good food cooking. There was plenty of snow, Christmas carols, and it all built to Christmas Eve Midnight Mass at Sacred Heart Church - an annual tradition. It was a great honor to be picked as an altar boy to assist at Midnight Mass. Since I lived close to the church and was frequently called in on short notice as a substitute for kids who didn't show up, I usually got the nod from Father O'Brien for Midnight Mass. In every series of life events there comes a payback time. Uncle George told me once, "We send and receive our own letters." Most of mine worked out to my advantage. After Midnight Mass, we returned home for hot chocolate and gathered around the tree with great excitement as my father distributed the presents that my mother had selected, shopped for, and wrapped. Most importantly of all, the family was all together and around me.

The holiday season would officially start just after Thanksgiving when Santa Claus made his first appearance, waving his way down Main Street, on the back of a fire truck with its lights flashing and siren howling. My sister Mary's husband, Paul Morin, took his two sisters and me to see the event each year. The firemen threw candy and small toys from the truck. Santa Clause waved

44

hello. And we ended the evening at Murnick's Cafeteria for hot chocolate and doughnuts.

The holiday season, however, didn't come to our house until the week before Christmas. My father believed you could wear the holiday out by excessive celebration, so he kept it to as few days as possible. We went out and bought our tree, for example, just a day or two before Christmas. By then all the good ones were gone and we ended up with some of the scraggliest looking excuses for a tree that you can imagine. Once, after my brother Leo got his license to drive, Dad sent us three boys down to Levi Lashua's lot near Central Fire Station in Fitchburg to pick out our tree. He gave us a dollar to pay for it and another fifty cents to celebrate with hot chocolates at Brook's Drug Store next door to Levi's. It was a cold and snowy night. Levi had little interest in leaving the shack where he sat with his wood burning stove, getting maximum heat from all the pieces of birch and pine trees he had trimmed off his customers' purchases. "You can have any tree that's still out there for seventy-five cents," he said. "Except the ones with the red tags on the top. Those are sold and awaiting pick-up." We went out to look for our prize. There wasn't much to choose from. The trees left on the lot were small, bent, skinny, and generally looking pathetic looking. The only one we saw and really liked was the nice, big, full spruce tree - with a red tag on top. We knew it was sold to someone else, but we decided to take it anyway. We removed the tag, told Levi we had found one that would do, loaded it in the car, and took it home.

My father took one look at it and said, "How did you find such a nice tree as that this late in the season?" That did it. We broke down and told him the whole nefarious story. He wasn't mad, just disappointed. Perhaps that was worse. "Now go take it back," he said. "Tell Levi what you did and bring home an honest tree for the holiday." We took it back. Leo told Levi the story and Levi was neither mad nor disappointed. He said he understood. He came out of the shack and helped us find a tree in the back that was only a little bit away from being acceptable. We brought it home. My father was pleased. The funny part of it was that when we got it up in the living room and decorated it with lights and tinsel and icicles, put Dad's illuminated five pointed glass star on the top, and Mother's celluloid

Santa and sleigh on the branches, it was one of the best trees we ever had.

Nana Ware would come into the living room when we were done and join us for cocoa and cookies. She couldn't see anything but she could hear and she could smell. She smiled as she said, "I can feel Christmas all around me."

We would sit there. Talking about times past and looking forward to the big day coming soon. The Crosley parlor radio would be playing Christmas carols in the background. We would then ask Nana to tell us a story about one of her Christmas memories of when she was a girl, back home in Ireland. One time, she told us the story of Danny Mack, the miser of Lixnaw:

The Miser of Lixnaw

"Quite the meanest man in Lixnaw was the wealthy landlord and farmer, Daniel McMahon. We called him Danny Mack behind his back. He was Irish enough, to be sure, but it was the English swells he catered to. He knew rightly enough where the money and power was. He couldn't do enough for them. He treated all of us in the village like dirt beneath his heels. My father used to say, 'He's one of us, but he acts like one of them. That's the worst of all.' We all knew what he meant, and nobody went near Danny Mack unless, God forbid, they had to.

Mr. McMahon loaned out money at very high rates. If you borrowed a shilling today, you'd owe him two shillings next week. God forbid you couldn't pay that back or he'd have the constable on you. Your furniture and kit would be in his barn within a fortnight. 'The law is always the law,' my father said, 'but it's not always fair and not always just. It's not always the right thing to do.' My mother said you can only hate someone you fear, and not everyone feared Danny Mack. My father said amen to that, but added, 'it's small consolation to be only hated by a few when the rest of the village despises you as well.'

Mr. McMahon lived like a miser too. His cottage was one of the most miserable in the village and he always looked unkempt and in need of a good wash. He had no wife or family to care for him. He was quite alone with his money, and though he had quite a lot if it too, they say he'd still jump right down a rabbit hole after a penny. Sometimes the children would bend down and hide behind the stonewalls when he passed along the village roads. Then they would call out their cruel rhyme:

'Dan, Dan, the dirty old man.
Washed his face in the frying pan.
Combed his hair with the leg of the chair.
Dan, Dan the dirty old man.'

Then they'd scurry away laughing before he could recognize who they were. Most often he'd grab a rock or stick and fling it after them with a curse.

Of course, I didn't know much of all this at the time. I was just a little girl of nine or ten in the parish school; this would have been around 1870. Mr. McMahon was just one more poor soul I'd see winding his way through the streets on my way to church or school.

One day near Christmas, the parish priest gave us a special assignment. We were to come next time with a story from one of our family or friends about their favorite color. What was it and why did they like it? It was a good question, and could have been a lot of fun, but I was small and busy. I forgot about it altogether in the holiday preparations going on. It wasn't until I was on my way to parish school with my friends that I remembered the homework task. I had not done my assignment. I had not asked anyone my question. Fr. Kavanaugh would not like that, and it would go hard for me at home as well.

I was walking along the road, wondering what would become of me, when I looked up and walking toward me was Mr. McMahon himself. I had an idea.

'Good morning, Mr. McMahon,' I said cheerfully. ''Tis a fine day. And would ye have a moment for a question?'

He looked at me warily. 'And what question would the likes of ye be having for the likes of me?' he asked.

'It's for school, Mr. McMahon. I was supposed to ask a family member or friend to tell me their favorite color and why they like it. I was hoping I could ask ye my question.'

47

'Oh,' he said, looking at me suspiciously, 'am I your friend then?'

'No sir,' I told him. 'I forgot to ask my family and friends and I'll get into trouble if I go there without my lesson. I thought I would ask ye.'

He laughed at that. 'All right, child,' he said, 'I'll be answering your question. My favorite color is…orange.'

Now I thought he was joking me. Orange was the color of the British, and the Irish who supported them. The Orangemen called themselves The Ascendancy, and had little to do with the likes of us. But it was an answer, and the only answer I had to carry with me. I said, 'Oh, like the fruit!'

'And what would you know about the fruit, child? Have you ever tasted an orange?'

'No sir, but I have heard about them and they are soft and juicy and sweet.'

'Aye, they are that,' he said, falling into step beside me. 'I go to Dublin now and again on my business, and I'll have one there. They grow them on the islands near Italy, you know' he continued, and they have them there for sale in the city markets well into the winter months. I like them for their taste and their rarity. It is a special treat for me to have an orange when I'm in one of the big cities.'

By this time we were near the school. I thanked Mr. McMahon for his time and for talking with me. I was happy that I could now make my report. Mr. McMahon waved me goodbye and into the class I went. I made a good report in class that day. The priest was shocked that I had interviewed Mr. Mack. He said it was unusual - but a good thing to have the views of different people. Mr. Mack, he commented, half under his breath, was certainly a different person.

Well, I told my parents what I had done. My father was amused. My mother warned me against talking to people I didn't know very well. She added, 'It does show that there is a little good in everyone.' My father harrumphed at that. He said, 'Well, maybe Mr. Mack will get a bit of time out of the sulfur pit that awaits him in the next life.'

The story doesn't end there, Nana said. "It was a while later, on Christmas morning, when there was a knock on our cottage door. My mother opened it and found no one there. On the doorstep was a bright cloth tied with a bit of twine. 'What is this?' she said, bringing it inside and undoing the knots. 'Mary, child,' she said, 'I believe Father Christmas has brought ye this from your new friend.'

And there, inside the cloth, was my very first orange."

The Gold Ladies

Nana Ware was not the only storyteller in the white house on Temple Street. My father told stories too. Sometimes on a 1940's Sunday morning before church, I would crawl into bed with my parents and he would tell me stories about what it was like growing up in West Fitchburg during the early 1900's. He told about his biggest Christmas when he got a homemade sweater, an orange *and* a penny flute. He still had the flute. In fact, I have it even now.

He told me how the men from the mills would gather in the woods at the foot of Temple Street and play cards; and how they paid him a few pennies to climb a tree and watch out for the police. His father heard about this part-time job as a lookout and went down there with a switch and marched him directly home.

He told me about the Massachusetts Blue Laws which forbad any kind of frivolous behavior on Sunday, the Lord's Day. Once, he and some friends went up to the schoolyard for a Sunday afternoon game of baseball. One of the neighbors saw them at play and called the police. The cops arrived in a patrol wagon and broke up the game, with a stern warning against breaking the law again. Playing baseball on a Sunday was clearly not something to be undertaken lightly.

Another story had to do with the big old Hannah Mills warehouse just down the road from our house. It was empty and spooky and it bothered me. The windows were covered with brown paper, and we used to try and guess what was inside. Once Dad said it might be a storage place for circus animals between shows. I didn't have too much confidence in that one. Then one day he walked me down to the warehouse and to the railroad tracks behind it. There, on the siding, puffing and steaming and waiting for a green flag, was a Ringling Brothers Circus Train. All the boxcars were brightly painted and decorated. If you listened carefully you could hear the movement and snarling of the beasts within. "They must have just made a pick-up from our warehouse," he said. I never did figure how he orchestrated that one, but he was a master of timing and willing to invest a bit of effort in the support of a good story. Creativity on short notice has always impressed me.

One time we went for a walk in the woods near our home. There was a little millpond there in Pio's Field that provided water for the paper mills on the roads below. Sometimes, if your timing was right, you could be there just as the water level built up on the dam. You could watch the first water come tumbling over the lip and down the spillway. First a few drops, then several spurts, and finally a steady stream of water that built and built until it was a little torrent. The water was close to the top this summer night, so we sat and watched it and talked. There was an ant in the spillway. As the water started over the top, he became confused as to how to escape it. The water soon surrounded him. Finally, he just charged into the water and struggled his way across the spillway to dry land. He must have been tired. He climbed slowly up the side of the spillway we were sitting on. I leaned down with my finger to flick him back into the water from which he had just escaped.

"Don't do that," my father said.

"Why? It's just an ant."

"It doesn't matter what it is," Dad said. "It's got a life, and it just fought for the right to live it. Leave it alone." I did what he said, and watched the ant crawl away on what was his second lease on life.

Although the Ware family seemed to specialize in original characters, Dad had some interesting folks on his side of the family too. I think I talk less about them only because we rarely got to see them. They were few in number and seemed to live mostly around Buffalo, New York. One of the strongest McManus family figures I

personally remember from that time was his mother's sister, Aunt
Bridget, who lived with her children in Buffalo, New York.

Aunt Bridget must have been about Nana's age at this time,
but she was as stiff and formal as Nana was easy going and plain.
Aunt Bridget had been housekeeper to one of the wealthiest families
in Buffalo for many years. The people she had served had all died out
without issue and the family story was that she inherited much, if not
all, of their sizeable estate. In retirement, Aunt Bridget lived
comfortably in Buffalo with her family. She had her own bedroom
and a sitting room, both of which were kept spotless by various family
members. Here she took her meals, entertained as she saw fit, and
issued various edicts and orders that helped keep the family in line. I
seriously suspect she drove them crazy but no one dared challenge
her.

When I was in fifth grade, my father decided that Aunt
Bridget may not have too many years left and it was time to see her
one last time. We drove out to Buffalo for this once-in-my-lifetime
family visit.

Aunt Bridget was a severe looking woman, and meticulously
dressed in neat fashions from a much earlier time. To talk with Aunt
Bridget, I was told, was to learn how people behaved in the fine
houses during the late 1800's and early 1900's. I remember a long
black dress, almost like the habit our nuns wore, with a high collared
white frilly blouse and a black shawl. She was a formidable looking
lady. I was ushered into her sitting room, properly introduced, and
was allowed to kiss her cheek. She liked me. I could feel it at once.
She gave me a fleeting, slightly crooked smile. It must have been my
experience with Nana Ware, because what Aunt Bridget wanted most
of all was someone to listen to her talk. I should say to listen and be
interested in her conversation. I gladly sat by her chair and she told
me grand stories of her girlhood and her career in service that began
in a fine house in Boston and continued through many good years at
an estate in Buffalo. Frankly, I think the local family members were a
bit jealous of all the attention I received.

This went on for a day or two, and I genuinely enjoyed her
company. When it was time to go home, she called in my father and
directed him to a heavy, sealed carton on the floor of her closet. She

told him it was for me. It was something for "dear little Edward" to
have and remember Aunt Bridget by. My father couldn't have been
much happier. He never hoped for such luck. He beamed at me. The
carton was heavy and Dad had a bad back, but a little extra pain and a
spasm or two was a small price to pay for this great treasure. We
thanked Aunt Bridget profusely and beat a hasty retreat to our car
before the local family members got too inquisitive. After he got the
box loaded into the trunk of the car, my father almost killed us getting
back to the hotel. He carried the heavy thing inside himself (no
bellboy was going to get his hands on this) and up to our room.
There, with great excitement and anticipation, he cut off the numerous
rounds of twine that sealed it shut, ripped off the tape, and pulled back
the cardboard flaps. The carton was filled with old Catholic
magazines from the 1920's and 1930's. My father couldn't believe it.
He never swore, but this time he did say, "What the hell is this?" He
started pulling them out of the box. I think he hoped they might have
been packing material for whatever great treasure was hidden on the
bottom of that carton. Alas for him, under the old Catholic magazines
were more old Catholic magazines; hundreds of them. My father said
a bad word, and my mother corrected him. He sat by the window for
a while and my mother nodded that it was time to leave him alone.
We both flipped through the pages of a few of the many magazines
there were to choose from. Dad recovered within a few minutes. We
stuffed the magazines back into the box and he shoved it into the hotel
room closet. We grabbed our bags and left. Those old Catholic
magazines may still be there to this very day. If so, they are probably
collector's items by now.

Nana loved that story. I had to tell it to her two or three times
when we came home, dwelling especially on the part where my father
practically shredded the carton to get at its holy contents. It was
indeed one of my better story telling efforts, she told me, in
congratulatory terms.

But the tale doesn't end there. About a year later, Aunt
Bridget passed quietly away in her sleep. The Buffalo clan called to
notify my father of her death, and to ask if he would contribute to the
funeral expenses. Aunt Bridget was broke. She had lived
comfortably the last several years of her life on the love and

generosity of her family. If they had thought there was more to it than that, if there were wild and unfulfilled expectations, well that was their problem, wasn't it? She had never misrepresented herself nor made a promise that couldn't be kept. As Nana Ware said to me as she chuckled and patted my hand, "Ye came out ahead with the Catholic magazines now, didn't ye?"

The story of Aunt Bridget and the carton was not my father's favorite. The very best story my father liked to tell was about his grandmother, Honora, the gold lady. Honora is the long form of the popular Irish name, Nora.

"My Grandmother Honora," Dad said, "lived in that big farmhouse up at the top of what we now call Brick Mill. They owned a farm that ran all over that part of town and they had many men working for them. They were quite rich by the standards of the time. My mother, Mary Ellen, told me that on her sixteenth birthday her parents, Honora and Tom, gave her a Steinway Grand piano. That was an expensive purchase then just as it is now.

By the time Honora was middle aged she lacked for nothing. However, she had a family of children, grandchildren, nieces and nephews who wanted to give her presents on Christmas and birthdays, and other special times during the year. So, Grandmother Honora started her own family tradition: On each of those important days, she said, you could give her a gold coin. It could be whatever you could afford: one dollar, five dollars, ten dollars, even twenty dollars - they were all gladly accepted and the donors graciously thanked. She kept these gold coins in a stout old cigar box that she brought out only on the appointed days. I remember seeing that box when I was a little boy. It was so heavy she could barely lift it. No one knew if that was all of the coins or if she had taken some out and hidden them elsewhere. There was a lot of gold in that box. A small fortune and no one knew where she kept it.

Well, this went on for years and years until one day when I came to visit her alone. She didn't hear me knock or call out, so I walked into her sitting room to make sure she was all right. At first I thought she wasn't there. Then I heard the rumble that stones make when they rub against each other. I looked over at the old fireplace - and there she was, crouched inside it and reaching up the chimney. I knew at once what she was doing. There must have been a loose or missing stone up there inside the chimney. That is where she kept the gold. What a perfect hiding place! I went back outside and made some noise and then came in again shouting her name. She called me into her sitting room where I found her sitting in her chair with a book on her lap and a shawl over her knees. There was no sign of what she had been up to, and the subject was never mentioned.

The gift giving of the gold coins went on for several more years - even after my grandfather Tom died. A few years after that Honora herself died and that generation came to an end. There was some disagreement in the family over who would inherit what - but most of the discussion was about what happened to Honora's box of gold coins. They searched the house and barn from top to bottom but they found nothing. It was like the gold coins had disappeared off the face of the earth. It came out that my side of the family was not going to share in much of the estate and when I learned that I decided to keep my silence about what I knew. I still remember one uncle who I never really liked bringing me candy and saying kindly, 'You were close to Grandmother Honora. Where do you think she hid the gold?' I took the candy but I never told him a thing.

A few years later, the house and farm were sold to settle the estate. The new owners wanted to modernize it and they pretty much did over the entire house. This was now the 1930's and people wanted furnaces and central heating in their homes so fireplaces were out of fashion. They covered over the one in Honora's sitting room with a new wall and papered and painted it to look just like the other walls. That was around 1932. By now, nobody probably remembers there was a fireplace there at one time."

"And the gold?" I asked.

"I think it's still there," he said. "Behind the wall, up the chimney, under a loose brick. Maybe some day we will find it."

Of course, we never did. Not yet anyway.

I told this story to Nana Ware too. She loved it. She never had any gold coins I am sure but if she did, she probably would have done the very same thing that Great Grandmother Honora did.

"And if I find the gold," I asked her, "Is it mine to keep?"

"Well," she said thoughtfully, "it is your family's gold and ye have a right to a fair share of it. Ye would have to give some fair amount to your brothers and sister, at least. Whoever owns the house today may have some call on it too. It would be a difficult question. Back home in Ireland we would take it to the priest and ask him for a fair ruling on how to disburse it. Shall I tell ye about the time the village went to Father Kavanaugh about the stolen gold, the Tinker, and Agnes, the Witch of Lixnaw?"

And this is the story Nana told.

Agnes, The Witch of Lixnaw

"Agnes was not a witch at all," Nana began. "She was simply an old woman who lived alone in a neat and well-tended cottage just outside the village. All the children remembered her for her home baked bread on a summer's day. Ye could smell that bread baking for miles around. And if ye came near her cottage and called, 'Agnes, are ye baking the raisin bread today?' She'd say, 'Yes child, come in and have a slather or two.' And in we'd go. She'd have the soda bread with the raisins in it, and perhaps a bit of butter she had churned from the milk given by the old cow that lived behind her cottage. She cooked it all in the big cast iron skillet, and it was a great wonder that she could even lift it. Sometimes she'd have jam made from the fresh summer berries that grew on vines high and low all around her garden. She might have strong tea to drink, or a cup of cool spring water from the deep well outside the cottage. We would sit with her and talk and gossip and tell stories. Sure, it was a wonderful summer's day when Agnes baked her raisin bread.

Agnes was a seamstress. My mother said she was the best in all the county of Kerry. She could take a bit of cloth from a Tinker, or from a sack of seed and turn out a little dress the likes of which you might see in the shops of Dublin. Not that any of us had seen what was in the Dublin shops of course, but they were that good. She sold them for a few pennies, or whatever she could barter, in Lixnaw and all the surrounding villages. She didn't sell many, there were few enough pennies for food let alone clothes made outside the family, but Agnes would say, 'That's all right, then. Take the frock for the child

56

and have your man come over and fix that old handle on my pump and we will be even.' The people liked that arrangement. The men would come over and do this chore and do that chore for old Agnes. She would give them the fresh bread and the strong tea and they would stop and do something else to help out before they went home. That may have been why she had the best-tended cottage in the village.

And everyone liked Agnes, even if she was a bit odd. My mother said that could come from living alone. One thing she always did was go for walks in the woods and pick up small brightly colored little stones that took her fancy. No one knew why she wanted the little stones. I guess she just liked them. The ones that had bits of crystal in them she would put on the window ledge where the sun would catch them and make sparkles and little patterns on the clean white walls of the cottage. The rest she kept in a velvet bag she had made herself. Purple, it was, with a bit of yellow twine at the top. She kept it in the little hutch where she put the bread to cool.

Now some people, it started with the children, said that all those clothes she was making weren't just for the children. They were for the little people. She was the little people's tailor. They said she made the velvet hats and the buttoned tunics and pantaloons, and even the curly tipped shoes that the little people wore. Agnes, they said, must be a witch herself to have contact with the likes of them. They also said she must be very rich. Everyone knows the little people ask no favors. They pay for everything they need or take. And, they always pay in gold.

Stories like that get around quickly and get richer with the telling. Soon someone would say they had seen one of the little people sitting in her kitchen having jellied bread and hot tea while Agnes finished their suit. Someone even said she kept a purple, velvet bag with a bit of yellow twine at the top, filled with gold coins in the little hutch where she cooled the bread.

That was the story that caused the trouble. The story of Agnes and her bag of gold went all around the county until someone told it to the wrong person. Maybe a Tinker or an Englishman or a landlord.

And so, one dark night, this bad man crept into Agnes' cottage while she slept. He tiptoed over to her hutch and slowly opened the door. There was the velvet sack with the yellow twine on top, just as the story had it! The man felt the sides of the bag and smiled. Sure, you could feel the gold coins themselves through the velvet cloth. He took the bag over to the window and opened it to look inside by the moonlight. 'Ah,' he thought, 'look at the beautiful yellow coins shining in the light of the full moon. It's a king's ransom, it is.' And off he stole with his great treasure.

Well, he didn't get far. When he stopped at Mallahy's pub in the village, the men recognized Agnes' velvet bag. They held that man tight while others went out to see if Agnes was all right. She was, thank God, and she came back into town with them. They confronted the thief. Agnes opened the bag and took out a handful of her colorful little stones. 'And why would ye steal these?' she said, 'When ye can pick them up along the roads and stream beds like I did myself.'

The man was fearful. 'You're a witch!' said he. 'I felt those coins in the bag and I saw them shine in the moonlight. They were gold! Ye and your dealings with the little people. Ye have changed the golden coins all into little rocks!'

'And if I did,' laughed Agnes as she poured out the entire bag of little colored stones on the table, 'it's a good job of work I did too.'

Well, the men took the thief to Fr. Kavanaugh. He listened to the story and decided it wasn't worth turning an Irishman over to the English authorities for just stealing a bag of stones - even though in his heart he thought he was stealing something of great value. The priest said to let him go. He wagged his finger and told the fearful man never to come back to the village again. The men there told him a few other things that would happen if he ever did come back. The man swore a sacred oath that he would never set foot in the village again. Fr. Kavanaugh couldn't resist one more thought. With a twinkle in his eye he said, 'and if you're ever found here again, you'll be getting a bad spell cast on ye by Agnes herself, the Witch of Lixnaw.'

And the man left the village and was never seen again."

"And what about Agnes?" I asked.

"Oh," said Nana, "she was fine as ever. She still made her bread and jam of a summer's day. And the children sat with her and talked while she made little dresses for the village girls. She still collected every brightly colored little stone and pebble she saw along the road and in the little streambed. She kept them in her purple velvet bag with the yellow twine on top. She made the little clothes for the children all over the county, and nobody ever bothered her again. They said she was under the protection of the Church, the Little People, and the men of Lixnaw. And sure, no one was fool enough to court trouble with the likes of any of them."

Nana And The Magic Salt

My father hardly ever took summer vacations. He had a good job of long standing at Motor Tire Company, an auto parts supplier on Main Street in Fitchburg, and he was certainly entitled to a vacation. However, he never wanted to spend much time away from his own home: The white house on Temple Street. His parents had built it. It was everything that he ever wanted in a house, it was left to him free and clear, and he saw no reason to spend his money to stay some place else.

This pretty much meant no summer vacations. He took time off here and there throughout the year to work around the yard or make a day trip to the Brockton Fair to watch the oxen pulls and to stroll the midway, but he hardly ever took off one entire week at a time. It was rarer yet when he took time away from work *and* suggested we go on a trip.

That is why in 1943 my mother was shocked when he announced that he was taking a week off and we were all going to the beach at York, Maine. Mother loved the idea of a vacation at the beach. Although, as I heard her confide to Nana, with a husband and four children to care for, a week at the beach was just a "change of sinks." We all figured that we were due three meals a day, seven days each week, and we pretty much expected them to be prepared properly and on time. In addition, there were several clothes washings to be done in an old iron tub washer with the hand wringer and heavy, damp clothes that had to be hung outside to dry.

Naturally, there was housekeeping and shopping to be done. She certainly filled her days while we frolicked in the sand and surf.

However, my father had spoken and the decision was made for a vacation. We packed the big, black, 1938 Packard Eight (Massachusetts license plate 76864) with everything we owned. Then the six of us, plus Nana Ware, piled in the car and we headed for the ocean. I still don't know how we all ever fit in that car, big as it was. We had boxes of clothes, food, beach toys, bedding, even some silverware and china as Mom said you never knew what you'd find in a rental cottage—or what condition it would be in. As for the seven of us, this was the early Forties, well before the days of seat belts and safety consciousness. We just stuffed ourselves into that car. I remember crawling up on the little back window ledge behind the rear seat, and occupying that position for the next ninety miles, or three hours, whichever came first—assuming the Packard's radiator didn't boil over in the summer heat and traffic. If that happened, then we had to sit for an hour or two in the shade by the side of the road somewhere until it cooled down enough to resume the trip. My father kept a large jerry can of water in the trunk to top off the radiator once it stopped spouting off like Old Faithful. He poured it in when the steam had calmed down enough to allow him to get the cap off, and cooled off enough to tolerate the injection of more water. Meanwhile, one of my mother's baskets always contained a picnic lunch and a jug of lemonade for just such emergencies. It was quite pleasant actually. The only one who got upset was my father and since he went quiet and kept to himself when he was upset, he never really bothered the rest of us with his concerns—outside of a muttering undercurrent that we never really listened to anyway.

The cottage was on Nubble Light Road, just around the corner from Long Sands Beach in York, Maine. It sat on a high cliff and offered a fantastic view of the Atlantic Ocean. You could hear the surf breaking on the rocks and beach below. I remember the roar of the waves, the cry of the gulls, and the aroma of salt air, seaweed, and the musty-wood smell of the wainscoting in the old cottage itself. The house was not insulated, so you could see the simple electrical wiring running between the studs to the light switches and electrical sockets. There were even candles and an old kerosene parlor lamp. It was wonderful. Dad walked us all down to the beach while Mom washed and dried every dish, cup, glass, and spoon in the kitchen cabinet. "You never know," she'd mutter cryptically, "You never know."

Each morning we'd be up with the sun and down on the beach where we would spend the entire day in the sand and surf. Dad would bring down a picnic basket at noon and we would all take lunch together on the sand under a big, old green canvass umbrella.

To our great surprise, Dad told us he was thinking of buying the cottage we were staying in. It turned out that was the entire reason for the trip. A man he knew wanted to sell him the house as a vacation home and investment. He offered Dad a week's free stay to show him how much he would like it. Dad was not a beach person. He could not abide the feel of sand on his bare feet for one thing, and he hated the bright sun for another. He would come to the beach in an open necked dress shirt, the pants from his suit, and business shoes and stockings. It did look a little strange, but no one took any notice and we certainly didn't care.

"It could be a good investment," he told my mother. "It's a seven room house right on the ocean and he's asking two thousand dollars for it. I think that's a fair price. The house will appreciate over the next several years. When the war is over and people start thinking about vacations again, it will go up even more. It could be worth eight or even ten thousand dollars by the time the children are grown. We could rent it out for fifteen or twenty dollars a week whenever we are not using it." It was an appealing argument and Mary, Leo, George and I were all in favor of it. Our views were always welcomed if not highly considered in the final decision making process. Dad made all the decisions.

Dad loved York, the house and the beach for the first two days we were there. Then he got bored. "Do you miss all your friends?" he'd ask us. He seemed to hope we'd burst into tears and demand to be taken right home, but our answers were usually along the lines of, "not really." By the third day, he was really bored. "We should think about getting home," he told my mother, "I'm not sure we'd like it here." Mom said something like, "I wouldn't know, I haven't been out of the kitchen since we got here." But her subtlety was lost on

Dad. He just didn't pay much attention to anyone when he felt their conversation smacked of negative thinking.

That afternoon, my father was talking to Mattie, the lobsterman who kept his traps in front of our cottage. He sold Dad lobsters fresh from the sea for twenty-five cents each. "Is the owner trying to sell you the cottages?" Mattie asked my father.

Dad came instantly alert. "Yes, he is," Dad replied, "is there any reason I shouldn't consider his offer?"

"Oh no," said Mattie, "it's a fair offer, all things considered. He owns your house and the one next to it as well and he has both of them up for sale. You might even get a little better deal if you offered to take the two of them. He doesn't want to be worried about the U-boats, you know."

"U-boats?" Dad asked. "What U-boats?" We all gathered around. This was wartime and even I knew a U-boat was a German submarine.

"The German U-boats, of course," Mattie said. "Just last spring they found one surfaced in the fog just up the road there by Nubble Lighthouse. Brazen as can be, they were, just sitting on the surface charging their batteries and taking in air. One of the boys spotted them and called the Coast Guard down in Portsmouth. They had a Navy destroyer just sitting there in the harbor, big as life. The Navy got that tin can cranked up in record time. It came steaming up here at top speed, bristling with guns and bombs and howling that claxon cry that only them big ships can make when they go on the attack. Ah, it would send shivers down your spine.

"The Germans, of course, knew they had been spotted. They submerged and set out to sea towards Boone Light, just two miles off the coast there. The destroyer was right after them, hot on their tail. They got some electric thing that can spot U-boats under water, you know. Well sir, that destroyer just went back and forth, up and down, sideways and back, dropping depth charges wherever they thought that submarine might be. You could hear the explosions and see the great plumes of water rising up from the sea. They figure they got it too. Can't prove it, of course, but they figure they clobbered it good. Raised an oil slick, they did. That submarine is probably out there right now. That's why the old man wants to sell, of course. He

63

figures the Germans will come back and shell these houses along the beach to pay us back for what we did to their submarine."

"Shell the houses?" My father asked, horrified. "The houses we're staying in?" We were all listening intently now.

"Yup," Mattie continued, "the Germans got those big guns on the dreadnaughts, like that Bismarck, and you read about in the papers. They say they can hit you without even seeing you. The boys who work at the Portsmouth Navy Yard say they could stand offshore a mile or more and just level everything that stands along the beach. Some of the folks worry about that."

"That does it," said my father, "we are going home." He marched us up to the house and told my mother we were leaving. He set us packing while he rode into town with Mom to see the man who owned the property. Mom told us that part of the story later.

"That house you want to sell me is going to be shelled by the German navy?" My father asked him. "You never mentioned that to me."

"I don't know whether it is or isn't," said the old timer. "I don't want to be a part of any of it. I did my bit in the last war. My price is fair and I'm sorry you are upset. I tell you what I will do. I own the cottage next to yours as well. Do a deal with me right now, this very minute, and you can have the both of them for two thousand dollars - total."

"I wouldn't take them for fifty cents," my father said, storming back to the Packard, "We are going home!"

And home we went. It was the best of both worlds for my father. He got to do what he wanted to do all along, and also was able to cloak it in high purpose. He somehow wove together the safety of his family with the security of the American shoreline, and a pox on the German Navy. It all sounded like the right and patriotic thing to do.

We told stories on the way home among ourselves. George was sure he saw a periscope just out past the breakers on Long Sands. Maybe it was the Germans watching us swim. Leo saw marks on the beach one morning that could have come from a rubber raft dragged ashore. My sister Mary just listened and smiled at us but never said a word. It was all a very exciting time, but reality soon set in and later

64

that day we were back home on Temple Street, unpacking the car and adjusting to the daily routine once again.

Nana hadn't said much about all this. She did not interfere with major family decisions taken by my father. The only thing she said to us was, "Ye be sure to say a prayer tonight for those boys in the U-boat. They had mothers and grandmothers too, ye know."

Later that night, we talked about vacations, the ocean, and the senseless things that people do when they don't use their heads for the good judgment and common sense that God expects of us all. I asked her if she knew any stories about such people and the ocean. As luck would have it, she did:

The Famine And The Salt

"When I was a girl, back in 1870 or so, we always had enough to eat on our little farm. My father worked for a wealthy farmer and part of his payment came in what they grew. We always had potatoes, wheat for the bread, and one or two other vegetables, along with eggs from the chickens. It was a good enough life, and we did not expect much more.

Sometimes my mother would tell us what it was like for the people back in the bad times. The Great Famine they call it now. One day all the potatoes throughout Ireland turned blue and then black and rotted in the ground. No one knew what was causing it. The farmers thought it was a bug of some kind, or something in the air. But still, there were farm people who spoke of magic, and curses, and the wrath of the Little People. Whatever caused the blight, the potatoes were gone, and there was no food. People got sick and died in great numbers. The lucky ones had family in America who sent them money for passage. Soon all the young people in the villages were heading for America to get jobs to feed and raise their families. It was hard times.

It wasn't easy for the Irish over here either. There were people here in America who didn't want the Irish taking the jobs they thought were their own. Though they themselves might have come here just a generation before, now they were Americans and we were foreigners and they wanted no part of us. I remember when I came

here years later a few of the old businesses still had signs on their
gates: 'Help Wanted - N.I.N.A.' That meant, 'No Irish Need Apply.'

"How could they tell who was Irish?" I asked.

Nana smiled and sang a little piece from her song "Erin Go
Bragh." The part where the policeman tells Pat, 'I know you're a Pat
by the coat that you wear. I see you're a Pat by the cut of your
hair…'

"Things got worse back in the village of Lixnaw," she
continued. "Most of the land was owned by people who lived in
England and a pestilence and famine in Ireland did not mean much to
them. They still wanted their rents paid every week. The people had
no food, no money, no jobs - and a landlord with his hand out for the
rent money. The law was on the landlord's side. Most of the people
lost their homes, got sick, starved, and many died. It was dreadfully
bad.

My mother told me what mothers did to help the children.
They took little scraps of the good food like meat and eggs, when they
could get them, and put them in a jar on a shelf near the table. Then,
when the children would eat whatever little bit of food they could
find, they could point their spoon at the food in the glass jar on the
shelf and pretend what they were eating had that taste. They added a
bit of pepper to the drinking water to give it flavor. 'Kitchin,' they
called it. It was all very sad.

The ones who lived near the sea were the lucky ones. They
had the fish, ye see. Also, the men would climb the cliffs along the
shore at night and get the birds' eggs, and sometimes the birds
themselves in order to keep their families alive. They ate dillisk, the
seaweed, and used it to bake their bread when they could find no
other fixings.

They told the children stories to pass the time. They were
stories about things to eat, the ocean, the evil landlords. One of them
was about the magic salt machine.

We all need salt, ye know. 'Ye must earn your salt by the
sweat of your brow.' The Bible tells us that. If we didn't have salt we
would lose all the water in our bodies. The salt keeps the flesh moist
so the blood can flow and we can breathe and talk and live.

Well, many years before there was a man in the village who sold salt to the people. And he sold it at a fair price that was a great comfort to them. And then one day, there was no more salt. It had dried up and gone and the man had nothing to sell. The people had none to use. It was another great tragedy.

The man went to the Little People who live in the forts and the mounds and he told them what had happened. He said right out it was help they were needing and not any more of their tricks. The Little People liked that. Everyone respects a person who is honest and direct in their speech. They knew him to be a good man and the village to be good too. So they gave him a magic salt mill. It was a small machine they had made in the woods and when ye turned the handle, salt came out. And it came out for as long as it needed to, just as long as ye turned the little crank. So, the man was back in business with his salt. The people in the village would wait for him each week until he came by with his magic machine and they would turn the crank for as much salt as they needed for themselves and the animals. Then they'd give him a penny to live on, and off he would go to the next village.

Well, the landlord soon heard of this magic machine. He knew the people needed salt, and he knew they would have to pay more than a penny for it if he had that salt machine. His greed took control of his life. 'And why then,' he asked himself, 'don't I have that machine? I could just take it, and there is none to stop me.'

And that is what he did. He and his bullyboys went to the little man's cottage and took the machine away from him, and there was nothing to be done about it.

'And why should I waste my time with selling salt to the likes of the poor people in this village?' he thought. 'They have no money. I could sell more in Dublin. Better yet—I could sell it in London, that's where the money is. The Swells will pay dearly for my salt.' And he hatched a plan to sail for England with the Little People's magic machine and make his fortune.

"But the Little People know such things, ye see. And as the greedy landlord set sail for England, they put an enchantment on their little machine. And when his ship was far out to sea, the little machine started up by itself and began producing salt. The landlord was amazed at this. At first he was excited. 'Sure, I'll have salt to spare by the time we reach London,' he said.

But the little machine would not stop. More and more salt came out of it, filling first his cabin, then the hold, and then the deck of the boat carrying him. He tried to shut it off, but the enchanted machine would have none of it. It kept producing salt, more and more salt, until the boat was filled with salt and riding low in the water. Oh, now the landlord saw his evil ways and his fate. He prayed to the God above for mercy. 'Save me!' he cried, 'for I am a good man at heart.' But he was a wicked man at heart and, as ye know, the prayers of the wicked availeth nothing. Soon the ship was awash with salt, and it sank into the waves under the weight of all that the enchanted machine produced - and the greedy landlord with it. He was never seen again."

"And is that how the ocean got so salty?" I asked.

"I didn't say that," she smiled, "but it is a pious thought and worthy of consideration. What matters is this: The poor are the favorites of both God Himself and the Little People. All wrongs against the poor are avenged in this life or the next, and sometimes in both. And if ye hurt or cheat the poor in your greed for wealth and power, there won't be a hole in the ocean deep enough for ye to hide in.

The end. Did ye like that story?"

Nana, George, And The Trouble

The white house on Temple Street, like the rest of West
Fitchburg in the 1940's, was in a warm and privileged time warp - at
least as far as the children were concerned. We knew about the war in
Europe. We talked about it at St. John's grammar school, heard our
parents discuss it, and listened to reports about it every night on the
radio. We even saw newsreel films of the action when we went to the
movies each Saturday afternoon at the Fitchburg or Lyric Theatres for
the double features, short subjects, cartoons, and previews that could
keep us there the better part of four hours. We purchased all this
entertainment for (as the sign on the box office read) "Under
Twelve—12 Cents."

I remember listening to the short wave band on Dad's Crosley
radio one Sunday afternoon when a Mr. Churchill was speaking from
London about the war over there. He was a very dramatic speaker
and although I didn't understand much of it, Dad was very impressed
both with what he said and how he said it. "The man is an orator,"
Uncle George agreed, listening from behind the newspaper he draped
over his head when he tried to nap. "What a change from my time!"
he might say. "Now we listen to London on the parlor radio, no less.
Back in the Great War, Christ himself could have come to Boston and
we wouldn't hear about it fifty miles away in Fitchburg." My father
grudgingly accepted the concept but cautioned him against the use of
strong language in front of the children.

Once in while we had air raid drills. The mills would blow
their whistles, the city would sound the fire alarms, and we would
have to turn off all the lights in the house to guard against guiding the
enemy bombers that thankfully never came. Mr. Vickery, the
neighborhood air raid warden, would come around in his bright silver
helmet and warn anyone showing a light to put it out now. My father
would put a newspaper over the illuminated dial of the big Crosley
radio console in the living room so he could listen to what was
happening in the outside world without the dial light giving away our
position to the Germans who might be overhead at any moment. In
addition to the AM stations, that Crosley had short-wave reception, so
he could literally listen to stations from around the world. It was all
very exciting, but it was just practice, like a school fire drill. We were
safe and we knew it. The war seemed very far away indeed.

Nana's sons had all served in World War I and she never
understood why that war didn't solve the problem once and for all as
everyone had said it would. "The war to end all wars, it was called,"
she sniffed, "Indeed."

The principle soldier among Nana's sons was Uncle George,
my mother's older brother. He had come out of the Spanish-
American War as a sergeant in 1889 and went into the 26th Division
National Guard in Fitchburg. The Guard was not then as close to the
Regular Army as it later became when it merged with other state units
to form the famous Rainbow Division that led the way into France
under the command of Black Jack Pershing. At first, the Guard
trained with broomsticks instead of rifles, used outdated equipment
from the last century, and generally was considered something of a
well-intentioned joke - until the war broke out. Then they became the
army's shock troops. The mission of the Guard in those days, Uncle
Georgie told us, was to buy time. They bought time for the Regular
Army to recruit, train, equip, and transport the professional soldiers to
the trenches of France where the war was raging. "Our boys were
gun fodder," Nana used to say, angrily.

Uncle George didn't say too much about what happened in
those hellish trenches over there in France. I later heard he was at
Verdun, Chateau Tierney, and several of the other war time hot spots.
Nana said he was both gassed and shot. He got a battlefield

commission to First Lieutenant and became a Company Commander. I learned that much. Years later, in the Fifties, when I went into the Army and told some of the older sergeants about that, they were impressed. "The officer corps was a closed club in those days," they told me. "For an uneducated, mill town, Irish Catholic to make the officer ranks and command a company - well, he must have been something special." He was. Even in his later years he was a striking six-footer with a proud carriage. A loving man with a rough edge, he liked a drink and a story.

Once he told about the Irish kid he put on sentry duty outside the company area. He told the lad no one was to be admitted without written orders. Naturally, later that night a major showed up without orders and demanded admittance. The lad said no. The major attempted to push his way by the soldier, but the lad stood firm. He said, "Major darlin', if ye go by me now, do I have to kill ye or is it all right just to shoot ye in the leg?" The major decided to wait outside until assistance was called. He later reported the man for insubordination to Uncle George. "And what did ye do?" asked Nana. "Why, I bought him a drink," laughed Uncle George.

His favorite joke when he visited was to send me into the kitchen to tell my mother he was hungry and wanted a 'soup sandwich.' She always laughed at his jokes to help lift him out of the depression that haunted him constantly. As I grew older, so did his stories grow more mature. Once he asked me in front of my father, "Edward, do you know the difference between a horse's ass and a mailbox?" I said I did not. "Well then," he laughed, "I'll never ask you to mail a letter!" My father was outraged. "He can't come into my house and tell the children rude stories," he complained to my mother. She agreed to have a word with Georgie. I'm sure she never did. It wouldn't have helped anyway.

One of the family time bombs he planted was with my older brother George. The boy was named after Uncle George and was quite his favorite nephew. He would stop in during the work day when my mother was feeding George and offer to spoon feed him the vegetables my mother had cooked and mashed for his lunch. Brother George grew up hating squash. He never understood why, but he hated it. Years later something triggered a memory and he recalled

71

the big old man who was feeding him saying, 'George, my boy, don't let anybody feed you squash. It looks and tastes like caca." Brother George is now over seventy, and is still repulsed by the sight of squash.

There weren't many funny stories Uncle George could tell about the war in the trenches. Those stories, I understand now, were too difficult to remember and too horrible to tell. Someone told once about a body that was buried in a trench with one hand sticking out. The men left it there and shook hands with it for luck whenever they went out on a mission. My mother said Uncle George came home from World War I a broken man, much changed from the high-spirited, alert young athlete he had been. "It was only around the children that he regained a bit of his fun for a short time," she told me once.

There is one other Uncle George story I remember:

Uncle George came to our house every Sunday noon for the weekly big family dinner and get together. My mother returned from early Mass at 7am to spend the rest of the morning preparing a huge meal built around a ham, roast, chicken, or whatever was available at Tucker Brothers grocery store that weekend. Meat was rationed in those days and you just made do with what you could afford and what was available. The only family I knew who had meat all the time was the Muldoon's. Bernie Muldoon was my neighborhood friend and he would tell me how every Sunday morning, his grandfather would take the old Hudson Terraplane and circle the roads around Fortune's Chicken Farm up the road in Westminster. Invariably, some poor hapless chicken who had escaped through the fence would wander into Grandpa Muldoon's path with the inevitable consequence: a squeal of brakes and a dead chicken. Grandpa would stop the car, get out and inspect the damage, then say sadly to the boys, "What a tragedy this is. However, the damage is done and there's no sense in letting the poor fellow just lie there." Off he'd drive with the chicken and, once again, the family had their Sunday dinner.

When I grew older and got my license, it was my job to pick Uncle George up at his apartment and deliver him to the Temple Street homestead. There he would sit at mother's mahogany dining room table in his three-piece suit with the gold watch chain, shirt, tie, and with a pack of Pall Mall and a pack of Lucky Strikes in front of him. Between dishes, or during breaks in the conversation, he would chain smoke: First a Pall Mall, then a Lucky Strike. He would make it through most of both packs before dinner had ended. There was always a heaping full tray of ashes and butts beside his plate.

I never saw anyone who could inhale a cigarette like Uncle George. With the intake of one single deep breath, half the length of the cigarette would disappear into ash. With the second breath, or certainly the third, it was gone entirely. Once in a while he would go into a prolonged coughing fit during which he talked and swore to himself half aloud. "Shut up you damn fool," he'd say. My father would just shake his head and say, "George, someday they're going to have to chip that stuff out of you."

Uncle George could tell a rough joke at the drop of a hat, and used a few inappropriate epithets from time-to-time. I think now he did that mostly to irritate my father whom he thought was a little too serious for his own good. However, Uncle George never took the Lord's name in vain. He drew the line at that. Nothing offended him more than hearing the Lord's name used in a casual or inappropriate way.

Once, after I picked him up at the Crescent Apartments, a car ran a stop sign and pulled out of a side street ahead of me. I almost ran into him. "Jesus Christ!" I said, slamming on the brakes.

There was no accident, but I knew I had crossed Uncle George's line. I waited for his reaction. After a time, he quietly began this way: "I said that once. We were in the trenches outside of Verdun waiting for the whistle to go over the top and attack the Germans on the other side of the field. What we didn't know, of course, was that the Germans were sitting there just like us, waiting for the signal to cross the field and come at us. There was artillery overhead and gunfire on all sides and the trenches were filled with both morning mist and smoke. I heard a scrunch just a few feet from me, like someone had jumped into the trench with me. I turned to look and it was a German soldier, coming at me with a bayonet. I swung my rifle around and fired. I said, "Jesus Christ!" I am sorry now I took the Lord's name, but I thought it was appropriate and that I would be forgiven in that particular case."

I never took the Lord's name near Uncle George again.

Sometime during the Sunday visit, he would go sit with Nana and they'd have their Sunday ritual. "George," she'd say, "did ye go to Mass today?"

Uncle George would reply with the punch line of his joke about what the Irish widow was told by the pastor when she tried to arrange her poor husband's funeral: "High Mass for High Cash, Low Mass for Low Cash, and No Mass for No Cash."

"God forgive ye, boy," she'd say, taking a swipe at her 60-year-old son with her cane, "my own prayers will not be enough to save ye."

Nana's oldest daughter, my Aunt May, lived not far from us, and all of her sons were in World War II. They were Nana's grandsons and she prayed for them day and night: Victor, Phil, Ralph, Richard, and Jack: The whole family. She and my cousin Peggy were at home alone with a flag in the window that bore five blue stars for the five boys in the service. Every week Aunt May, or Peggy, would be up to see Nana with the latest word from the boys. They would read her all the letters while she thumbed her beads, shook her head intently and often cried. I remember when she heard the letter about Cousin Richard. He too was fighting in France against the Germans, just as Uncle George had done. He had been wounded and separated from his unit. He found shelter in an old barn, crawled up in the hayloft, and fell asleep. When he woke up, he found a German patrol had come in during the night for shelter as well. They were asleep all over the floor just below him. Somehow, he got out of there without disturbing them and got back to his unit for treatment. He won a Bronze Star for all that. "A miracle," Nana said, "a miracle for my boy."

Once when we were alone, and talking about the wars she called The Great War and now this one, The European War, I asked her if there were wars in Ireland when she was a child too. She smiled at that. "Sure, there were always wars in Ireland; wars great and small." She told me this story:

74

George And The Night Riders

"There was nothing but war in Ireland when I was growing up," she began. "We were an occupied country, ye know, occupied and ruled by the English. They had the land, the money, the power, and the law. There was little we could do but resist, and resist we did.

The problems were worse in the cities, but even in the little villages like Lixnaw we had our problems too. I remember when I was a little girl, there was a priest in our town that protested the way people were manhandled and how they could lose everything, including their home, and be turned out into the cold for the slightest infraction of English law. They warned him to be quiet, but he would not listen. He could not be quiet. Then one night they shot him down in front of his own church, and left him there for the people to see on their way to Sunday Mass. It was the Tinkers, the authorities said. The Tinkers killed him. Sure, no Tinker ever killed a priest. That would have brought down the Curse of God upon them. Whatever problems they had, the Tinkers were God fearing people who respected the Church. A Tinker would go bury himself in a peat bog before he'd lay a hand on one of God's Anointed ones.

"There was a young man near our village. His name was George. A fine, strong man he was, and a master horseman. He worked for one of the wealthy English landlords, as did most of our men in the village, for there was not much else to do. This foreigner had a horse farm where he raised those beautiful Arabian horses for racing and for show. They sold many of these fine animals to the British Army as show horses and cavalry horses. The Brits know quality when they see it, and Irish horses are among the finest in the world. George worked for this lord first as a jockey, then as a trainer and groom. Many are the times he wore the farm's orange and green racing silks and brought the prize home to his stable. He was that good.

When he was a trainer, he used to say, he would think what a good job that horse handling would be for a woman. 'These beautiful beasts,' he said, 'will follow anyone who gives them a smile and a pat and a soft word. They like a woman's gentle touch. If you try to act the tough and grab the bridle, or give them a shove or a kick, they'll show you who is the tougher. And a well muscled, intelligent animal two feet over your height and five times your weight can teach you a very hard lesson indeed.'

George wanted to come to America and go out to the Wild West. He wanted to be a cowboy. He had read all the books and heard all the stories about life on the American frontier. He had friends who had gone there and they wrote him what a free and glorious life it was, and how a man like him, with his gift for the horses, could make his fortune on one of the big ranches. It was his dream, and he saved every bit of money he earned for his passage aboard ship in another year or two.

The times were tough, as I say, and George got drawn into the Trouble. That is what we called the scuffle with the English occupiers: The Trouble. Most of the young men got drawn in one way or another. George became a Night Rider. This was part of the Sinn Fein movement. That means "Ireland Forever." They rode by night and tried to help the people where they could and let the oppressor know that even though they had the law on their side, their evil deeds would still be punished and wrongs they committed would be put right. The landlords and the foreigners came to fear them.

It seems the whole British Army was in Ireland at that time. The Brits are strange people in so many ways. They love their army when they need then but, after that, they'd just as soon the army went away. They don't like them too close. So, the old Queen sent the whole army packing off to Ireland where they'd be out of sight, but close enough to answer the call if they were needed.

The British Army was charged with keeping Ireland in its place. They knew about Sinn Fein. The English knew all about what was happening but were hard pressed to do anything because they did not have the support of the villagers, and they didn't know who these men were. But sooner or later, everyone knew the names would come out. There is no such thing as a secret, ye know. Everyone has someone they trust, and the story goes round and round, growing wider and wider, until it comes to the wrong ears.

So it was on a soft summer's night that the English found out about young George. He had been out that night with the men giving notice to a landlord that he could not just turn families out into the road and burn their cottage without answering to someone. George was riding back to the horse farm when he noticed his young sister, Molly, with whom he lived, waiting for him by the gate.

'The soldiers are waiting for ye in the barn, George,' Molly cried. 'I brought your money here in this cloth, along with my own little savings. Take it all and go now. Go to America while there is still time.'

George gave her a hug and a kiss, and swung the big horse around and started back out the gate. The English saw him leaving and leapt onto their own fresh mounts and came after him in full pursuit. They were yelling for him to stop in the name of the Queen. Alas for them, their fresh horses were no match for the big Arabian, tired as he was. And they themselves were no match for young George as a horseman. He soon enough put the distance between them, and he was lost to them forever. George rode to the port in Cork and booked passage aboard a freighter to Liverpool in England. Ah Liverpool, that's where the big ships were, readying themselves for the trip to America. He found the first ship that was leaving port and booked his passage among the other Irish in third class - they called it steerage. He said it was a long and sad journey, and he spent as much of it as he could at the railing, thinking about the one life fading away behind him, and the other looming up before him. Too much time for thought about the past, and not enough time for plans about the future, but it brought him to America, right here in the Port of Boston. That's where he began his life in the new world."

"And did he ever go out West and become a cowboy?"

"No, he didn't," she smiled. "He met me at the Dunne's Sunday afternoon tea social, and we soon fell in love and married. He became the best teamster in the area and drove those big rigs at the mills and for wealthy farmers at all the fairs and horse shows around the countryside. So he did keep his love of horses too, along with his new country and new family.

He was your grandfather, don't ye know."

Agnes, The Witch of Lixnaw
and The Enchanted Garden

On hot, summer days in the late Forties, we would take our bicycles up the long Church Hill, past St. John's grammar school, over Phillip's Street and up Ashburnham Street Road to the Boucher family farm. There were five Boucher brothers. The two oldest, Lawrence and Robert were in school with me. When they weren't busy working around the garden or cleaning the chicken coop or the rabbit pens, we would spend our time swimming, playing games, and doing light chores around their family farm. Many an afternoon we spent riding on the back of a rickety old tractor, or sullenly pulling weeds in the garden, so that by mid-afternoon we could sit down in the shade of the big old oak tree for a feast of fresh garden vegetables like tomatoes, cucumbers, and scallions. The veggies were topped off by watermelon and cold water from the deep, dark well in the barn.

They had corn growing there too, at least a couple acres of it. In mid-summer, I managed to be present for their annual "first corn" ceremony, usually on a July evening. A dozen ears would be selected from the first crop and rushed from the field into a large pot of boiling water. In ten minutes this fresh corn would be served up on a large steaming platter for Mr. Eli Boucher himself. Eli got the first dozen all to himself. The family would stand around the table quietly and observe the ritual. Mr. Boucher, without conversation or assistance, would eat the entire one dozen, drowned in fresh butter and sprinkled with salt, all by himself. Then, like Bob Cratchit and the Christmas

78

pudding, he would pronounce the corn crop a success and the entire family would turn to and cook up all the fresh-from-the-field corn they could eat. As an honorary family member, or at least chief hanger-on, I had my share of fresh corn right along with them.

When I got home, I would check in with Nana and she would ask about my day. I would tell her about the great adventures of working, eating, and playing on the little farm. I thought seriously about becoming a farmer when I grew up. The work is not too hard, I volunteered.

"Aye, the work is not too hard, that's the truth, but the work never ends," said Nana. "From sunrise to sunset and beyond, there is always something to be done on a farm. If ye let the work get ahead of ye, there's no catching up to it. For there are just enough hours in the day to get it all done, but not a minute more to do the bit extra.

In our village of Lixnaw, we had a grand little farm that was owned by Mr. Tom Doyle. A hard worker he was, and the little farm was green with the grass for the neat flock of sheep and herd of cows he kept. The chickens laid all the eggs he could use and gave him enough to sell besides. The fields were full of the vegetables he loved to grow, all in their neat rows with nary a weed to be seen. A generous man was Mr. Doyle. He paid his laborers a fair wage and gave them a little plot of their own where they could raise a few things for themselves and their families with his seed and his tools. It was the finest and happiest little farm in the entire county.

And then one day Mr. Doyle, God rest him, passed on to his reward and the farm went to his oldest son, Young Tom. In those days, the oldest son inherited everything entirely, regardless of how many other children there were. It was the way of insuring the farms weren't broken up into so many small pieces that they couldn't support a single family, let alone supply the village with jobs and with their overages to sell or barter. They used to say that the oldest son inherits the land, the second son goes to war, that means he joined the army, and the third son found the Lord. That means he joined the Church. The daughters, of course, got nothing. The young women had to marry, enter the convent, live with the family, or support themselves making thread at the spinning wheel. They were called 'spinsters.'

The Nana In The Chair, And the tales she told
An anecdotal biography of Mary Dunne Ware (1860-1956)

Well, Young Tom was a fine boy but he was never the worker his father was. He was a bit of a dreamer and would sooner spend an afternoon chatting with his friends and laying about then he would work out in the hot sun of the field with the hired hands. He just let things go on as they were and hoped for the best. My father used to say there are just two kinds of people: The Workers and the Shirkers. I'm not one to criticize, but Young Tom was not a Worker.

It wasn't long before people noticed that the little farm was not as neat as it once was. The fences and posts were not being repaired, and the animals were roaming all over the hills. They didn't look as well kempt as they once did. The barn and the sheds needed work. The gardens themselves were choked with weeds that kept out the summer sun.

The farm hands were another problem. They spent too much time at Mallahy's Pub socializing when they should have been at work. When they started offering more of their vegetables for sale, even though it was clear they were working less hard and fewer hours, people wondered where the extras were coming from. It was a sad thing to watch, but Young Tom did nothing but play the squire and hope for the best.

By the third year, the farm was in sad shape indeed. It was badly in need of repair and though it was late spring there had been no crops put into the ground. A farm runs on money, ye know, and Young Tom's money was rolling out but nothing was rolling back in to keep the larders full. Tom knew something had to be done, but he didn't know what. His first stop was to visit the little cottage just outside of town where Agnes lived alone with the help of the Little People, as some said. The children loved her, but they still called her Agnes, the Witch of Lixnaw.

'Agnes,' he said, settling down with a cup of tea in her neat little kitchen, 'I need your help. The family farm will be lost this year unless some magic comes to help me. I need an enchantment. I need a magic potion to make me successful again.' And he went on and on telling her the whole story.

Now Agnes knew the whole story. Everyone in the village knew the whole story. But they didn't feel comfortable giving Young Tom advice until he was wise enough to ask for it. Ye can never tell a person what needs to be done unless they want to listen. Agnes knew that because Young Tom came to her and asked her opinion, he was ready to listen.

Agnes thought for a bit, sipping her tea from the grand china cups she kept for herself and her frequent guests then went to the little hutch where she cooled her home made bread. She rooted around a bit and then produced a purple velvet bag, tied with a bit of yellow twine at the top. She opened the bag and produced a handful of brightly colored stones and pebbles of various sizes, shapes, and colors.

'Here is your charm, Tom,' she said. 'Take these magic pebbles with you. Every morning at first light, when the cock crows, put one on each boundary of your farm. Then put one in the barn and in the storage shed. Then, go back before sunset and do it all a second time. When you have done this for thirty days and nights, and have a fine pile of pebbles at each spot, the magic will work and a solution to your problem will be near at hand.'

Well, it did not make a bit of sense to Young Tom, but who was he to question Agnes, the Witch of Lixnaw? Her with her ties to the Little People? He decided to do what she ordered starting the very next morning. He thanked her for her kindness and rode off with the purple velvet bag slung over the horn of his saddle.

And he kept his promise. It was hard getting up with the cock's crow. He had never done that before, but the next morning up he was up and out before the sun was full in the sky. He took the bag of magic pebbles and rode out to the farthest point of the farm. The farmhands saw him go by and asked each other, 'Is that Young Tom riding out to inspect the farm like his father did? Let's be off to work before he wonders where we are.'

After Tom had placed the pebbles around the land, he came back and placed one near the barn. He saw what terrible shape the barn was in. 'Fix that door,' he told one of the men, 'and get this place swept out. I wouldn't ask an animal to live in here with it in this state.' 'Yes, Tom,' said the man, and he hurried off to tell his fellows what happened and to set them to work fixing the barn.

That afternoon, before sunset, the men in the fields were breaking off early when Young Tom rode up again. 'There's still an hour left of the sun,' he said. 'Get at those weeds that are choking the crops. And tomorrow, get all the spring seed in before we lose the season.' 'Yes, Tom' they said, shaking their heads at the wonder of it.

Could he keep this up, they asked among themselves, or was this a one-day marvel? The next morning at sunrise, Young Tom was back. As he placed his magic pebble near the sheep pen he asked the shepherd, 'And what sort of herder are ye? Ye never acted this way when ye worked for my father. Give me that same courtesy. Don't ye see those broken fence posts that let the animals wander all over the hills? Fix them today. And I want those animals as well groomed and cared for, as they were when ye worked for my late father, God rest his soul. And I mean today,' Tom said plainly. 'Yes, Tom,' the shepherd said.

Well, to their wonder and amazement, Young Tom was back the next day again, and the day after that, and even on the Sunday before Mass. He missed nothing and the men got to know and respect him. 'We might as well do it right,' they'd say about a job, 'or Young Tom will be out here on his charger to tell us about it.'

And so, life on the farm got very busy indeed. The buildings and fences were repaired. The crops were in and cared for. The men worked a full day for a full day's wages. There was plenty of food growing for everybody. And Young Tom's farm was once again the pride of the village.

One evening, as Tom made his rounds of the property as Agnes had instructed, he counted the magic pebbles in each of his little piles. He had done this for ninety days and, as Agnes had promised, the charm had worked. His problems were in hand. Early that next morning he rode out to her neat little cottage and thanked her over strong tea and warm bread, with a bit of her homemade butter.

'I could not have done it, Agnes,' he said, 'without your help. It was your charm and the magic pebbles that drove away all the bad things that were happening to my farm and me. But what happens now? The magic pebbles are gone. What charms have ye that will keep me successful?'

And Agnes smiled at Young Tom. 'There was no charm, Tom,' she said. 'The magic was you. Ye were out there where the work was done, to see what needed to be done, and to make sure the men were working on it. It is not enough to own the farm, Tom, ye must work it. And ye must be seen to work it. Ye must know the land, the work, and the people - and they must know ye. And now they do. Keep up your rides and your interest, Young Tom, every day, and the magic will go on for a very long time indeed.'

Young Tom sat back and took in the glory of what Agnes said. It was himself all along. He did it all. He beamed at the wonder of it because he felt the satisfaction of a job well done. Agnes knew exactly what he was thinking. She patted his strong young hand with her old and gnarled hand and said softly, 'Old Tom must be proud of ye.' Young Tom smiled, and his eyes sparkled with the mist.

'And what can I do for ye, Agnes?' he said. 'I know ye don't take the money. But what of our produce? A supply of vegetables and eggs and such? We could have the boys out now and again to help with a chore or two? What would ye like?'

'Those are wonderful things, Tom,' she said, 'and I thank ye for them. But first of all,' she continued, pushing toward him the empty purple bag with the bit of yellow twine on top, 'I'd like my magic pebbles back. I never know when I might need them again.'

"And Young Tom was good as his word," Nana said. "He was out there with the men every day—doing his job as they did their jobs. And the farm grew and prospered and none of them, including old Agnes, wanted for anything for the rest of their days. The end. Did ye like that story?"

Nana And The Tinkers

Winter was a great time for outdoor fun and games in West Fitchburg during the early Forties. For one thing, there seems to have been a lot more snow than there is today. It started earlier, we always had a white Christmas, and it lasted longer into the spring. I suppose part of it was because traffic was lighter than it is today, and the snow that fell lasted a longer time on the roads. Usually the ground cleared just in time for a spring-like Holy Week and Easter, two big times in the neighborhood and church spring social season.

For another thing, the city cleared the roads differently back then. They didn't have the big scrapers and all the salt, so they used plows and sand instead. As a result, the cleared roads after a major storm had a well tamped base of dry, packed snow which was perfect for…sliding!

The white house on Temple Street perched at the top of a fair sized hill with a long and winding road snaking down from it, past the Hannah Mill where my grandparents McManus used to work, onto Westminster Street, one of the main roads into the downtown area. It was perfect for sliding. If we were lucky enough to get the day off from school after a snowstorm, the police would sometimes shut down that long back road to automobile traffic and give it over to the kids with their sleds long and short, toboggans, skis, ashcan covers, cardboard cartons, and whatever other travel accouterments would help them move downhill, unsafely if necessary, but most importantly at high speed.

84

We had a long Flexible Flyer, and my two older brothers and I had an established ritual. First of all, they had to take me sliding with them. Not an entirely agreeable rule, by the way, but it was established by my father so, there it was. Leo, the oldest brother, leader and thinker, would steer the sled. George, the middle brother, was the implementer. He did all the work. I was the youngest and didn't do much but go along for the ride and occasionally complain when things were not to my satisfaction. Whining was one of my best things. There are people today who even say—oh, never mind.

We would position the sled in the middle of the road with Leo at the controls, me just behind him hanging on for dear life, and George in the rear. At Leo's signal, George would push the sled down the hill as fast as he could and, just before he lost contact with it, jump on the rear position and the ride would begin.

Leo and George would have sanded the rust away and then waxed the sled's iron runners with an old candle. The sled would move smoothly over the hard packed snow. The first part of the hill was straight down. We'd pick up speed quickly, with the cold winter air blowing in our faces and throwing back bits of ice and snow churned up by the sled's sturdy iron runners. It was exhilarating.

At this point, the hill banked gently to the left. It was an easy turn but somehow Leo never managed to make it. We would fly off the road into a snow filled field where the sled would tip and I would sail through the air only to land and sink deeply into the soft, deep snow. With my heavy woolen snowsuit, rubber boots, hood and double mittens, I would sink like a rock. I could see nothing but snow. I felt as though I were buried alive. The yelling would begin, "Help! Get me out."

My brothers would answer, "We can't see you. Where are you?"

"Over here, now get me out!"

"Keep talking, we're looking for you."

This exchange would continue until I saw their faces smiling down on me in my hole in the snow. They would drag me out, brush me off, and say, "C'mon! Let's do it again!" Back up the hill we'd go; back down the hill we'd go; Leo would again miss the turn; I'd end up buried in the snow once more; They'd take their time digging me out - it went on and on.

Finally, my mother would come to the door and call me in. "You are soaked!" she'd say. She'd pull off the boots and snowsuit and find everything down to my underwear cold and sopping wet. I'd get a complete change of clothes while the ones I had on were draped over the radiator to dry. Then she'd usher me into the kitchen where Nana was seated at the table about to have her afternoon tea and buttered Graham crackers. There was an open place for me.

"And did ye go sliding with your brothers?" she'd ask.

"Yes, Nana, and they tricked me. Every time I was on the sled they'd miss the turn and I'd end up buried in the snow. I think they did it just to get me to go into the house. But it didn't work! I only came in when mother called me."

"Tricked ye, did they?" she smiled. "Aye, they can be tricksters all right. Good-natured ones, to be sure, but tricksters nonetheless. Ye'll be meeting tricksters all your life, some of them good, others not so good. And did I ever tell ye about the master tricksters of all time? We called them the Tinkers, and they roamed all over Ireland when I was a little girl…"

Nana And The Tinkers Fair

"The Tinkers were the Gypsies of Ireland. Some thought they were the last of the Old Ones who came to us so many years before and built the mounds and forts. They called themselves the Traveling People and they were always on the move from village to village in their colorful horse drawn wagons. The wagons were called carabans, and a mule or donkey did often as not pull them. The donkeys were more sure footed over the rough roads than the horses. They were also less likely to get stuck in the marshy areas near the bogs because they walk in a different, flat-footed way than do horses. Donkeys are strong and not very smart. My father, God rest him, would say, 'Ye need a few workers like that too: strong—and not very smart.'

The Tinkers had no place they could call home, except their wagons. Part of that was because they liked to live on the road. There was always something different to see and do and always some place different to be. Another reason for their travel was that the farming people did not trust them. The Tinkers were thieves, people said. 'They'll take anything that isn't nailed down.' I asked my own father about this one time and he smiled and said, 'Well, sometimes the Tinkers just find things before they get lost.' He used to joke about the Tinker who was asked by the parish priest if he was a thief. 'On my word, Father,' the Tinker said, 'I never stole anything I didn't want.'

If they went into the little general store in the village, Mr. Foley the owner would tell them, 'Just keep your hands in your pockets and whistle!' That way he'd know where they were and what they were doing. He hoped.

There were stories about them from the Seanchai too. They said it was the Tinkers who camped by the magic well on the Killarney meadows one night and left it uncovered when they moved on next day. Everyone knows a magic well flows until ye cover it. Well, the Tinkers left it uncovered and it flowed for forty days and forty nights. By the time people found out what happened and capped it again, the water had formed the beautiful Lakes of Killarney.

The Tinkers made their living by doing odd jobs for the farmers. When they came to our village, they would go from cottage to cottage offering to repair old pots and pans and make them like new again. They could put a new bottom on a burnt out pan, or a new handle on a broken kettle and make them good as new again. At least for a little while.

The farm people generally let the Tinkers in because if you kept them away, they might put a curse on you. That was very bad indeed. Your potatoes might die in the fields or the cow get sick and not give milk, or even - God forbid - one of the children might be taken ill with the fever. A curse was a very bad thing, then and now.

My mother said that everyone suffers from a curse. She said that God splits the bad wishes into three parts, with one part going to the accursed, the second part coming back on whoever pronounced the curse, and the third part going on the world itself. My father said the Tinkers' one-third of all those curses must have put them in sad shape before the Lord. 'Besides that,' he said, 'the people who curse are not the ones God would listen to anyway.' But curses were not a joking matter with the women and the Tinkers were allowed into the village.

One day, my father told us at supper that the Tinkers were in town, '…and they are up to something new,' he said. 'They are putting on a show in that little field next to the cemetery, just outside of town. They say for one penny you can see strange sights from all around the world. I hear they have a horse with its head where its tail should be, and a magic potion that will kill any fly that troubles your barn and lets you take the air of a summer night without the bugs all bothering you for the effort. They have a stick with only one end, and a man who does not cast a shadow, and…'

'We all want to go and see that show!' we cried and though my father tried to hush us and say it was too expensive for the family. It is clear he intended to take us there all along.

As soon as the supper chores were finished, we headed for the little field outside of town. It doesn't get dark until 10 or 11 o'clock at night in Ireland, so there was plenty of time to see the show. What a sight it was! I had never seen anything so festive and gay as the Tinkers had made up themselves, their wagons, and that little field. Their brightly painted carabens and their cooking fires ringed the field - and they even had torches mounted near the carabens to create a carnival atmosphere. There was fiddle music and a few of the Tinkers were dancing. Some of the older women offered to tell fortunes for another penny. My mother said Fr. Kavanaugh would not approve of that. We are only supposed to know the future as it unfolds for each of us in accordance with God's will. Fortunetellers might very well be in league with the Devil. The whole idea went against the Church itself. My father said the fortunetellers didn't know any more than we did and that it was all an act to cadge another penny out of us—but he didn't press the point with my mother and let it go.

There was a tent rigged up in the center of the field and the Tinkers told us that's where the show was. They said it contained things we had never seen before and would never see again. My father gave them the pennies it cost, and we went inside. The first thing we saw was the horse with its head where its tail should be.

'What is this, then?' my father said, 'it's just a horse standing backward in his stall.'

'And what would ye know of that?' said the Tinker in a
threatening way. 'There are things here ye cannot understand,' and he
gestured us on in an unfriendly manner. My father moved on because
he had the family with him, but I think it would have been different
had he been there with his friends.

I don't remember all the things we saw. One was supposed to
be the world's shortest giant and his friend, the world's tallest midget.
'They are just two regular men standing there,' my sister Nell said.
My mother hushed her and kept us moving along the line of things to
see.

One of the last stops was the man with the magic fly powder.
'It will kill any fly on your farm,' the Tinker told my father, 'and it
just costs one penny for the envelope full.'

'How does it work?' my father asked.

'You just take the fly,' said the Tinker, shaking one into his
hand from the little jar he kept on the table, 'sprinkle the powder on
him, let him go like that, and in a few minutes he will be dead.'

My father looked at him. 'Why don't ye just crush him while
ye have him in your hand?'

'Ah, that's the beauty of it,' said the smiling Tinker, 'ye don't
have to.'

We left the tent and my mother said it was time to go. I
wanted to stay at the camp and watch the singing and the dancing, but
my mother said we had been foolish enough for one night. Besides,
she said, they would want another penny for this and another penny
for that and we would soon be spent out of our money entirely. We
would go home. That settled the matter and we started down the road
to the village.

My mother was silent on the walk home, and we dared say
nothing that would further upset her. Then my father started to laugh.
'It was just the few pennies,' he said, taking her hand and making her
smile despite herself. 'And now they are gone and there's no way to
get them back, so we must save what we can from the experience. It
was a good lesson for all of you,' he said, pointing at us children.
'Everyone, even your father, can be taken in by tricksters when we
want to believe, and have a little fun, and some loose change is
burning a hole in our pocket. You'll be meeting Tinkers and their like

all your lives, so now ye know what to do about it. Just smile, be polite, hold your hands on your purse, and keep moving.'

My mother smiled and took his hand and we all talked and laughed as we walked home together like the fine family that we were.

And no Tinker has ever had another penny of my money since that day," Nana said.

Nana, Miss Ruth, And The Train To Dublin

We did all our grocery shopping at Tucker Brothers Groceries in West Fitchburg for as long as I can remember. Nana said she shopped there even before that. We had an account at the store and I remember being with my mother one time in the Forties when she settled it up at the end of the week. The bill was nearly ten dollars. She thought that was a goodly amount to spend on a family of just seven people.

The Tucker family owned the store all through that time and they were friendly people and honest merchants. Miss Ruth Tucker, the proprietor's niece, was a special case. She was certainly honest, and friendly to a point, but whether you were a customer or not, she expected everything to be done her way. She would plunk her ample frame into the office armchair by the cash register, with her book or magazine at hand, and then move as little as possible until the day was done and the store closed.

There was a little adding machine by her perch, with a long streaming tape of numbers coming out the top and a hand crank on the side that made it all work. Miss Ruth would use this machine to total up your bill. She would write the total on your slip. That was all the detail you got. No item pricing from Miss Ruth. Once I asked her if I could have that bit of the tape that covered the purchases I was picking up for my mother. Miss Ruth was horrified at the suggestion. "Certainly not," she said emphatically. Screwing up my courage, I asked why not. When she recovered, with indignation, from the shock of my having questioned her judgment, she replied, "Because it wastes my paper tape. When this roll of adding machine paper is filled, I re-roll it and use the other side. That way I get the benefit of two rolls of paper from the purchase of one. I couldn't do that if I was ripping the tape apart for every customer who wanted to check the machine, could I?" I was smart enough to realize I had lost this discussion, so I withdrew.

My mother always checked Miss Ruth's figures though. If she couldn't have a copy of the adding machine tape, she would insist Miss Ruth write the item prices on our bill so mother could add them up herself when she got home. They were almost always wrong. A few cents here and there, but that was a lot at the time. It was most often over the amount we should have paid. Back we'd march to Tucker Brothers and Mother would have the bill corrected while Miss Ruth sighed and fumed and blamed technology, the hand-cranked adding machine, for all her troubles.

Nana would hear all this from my mother and shake her head sadly. She was blind and had always trusted Miss Ruth's bills when she shopped there for her own family. "I probably bought them a new scale or two over the years," she would sigh. "Easy come, easy go."

My favorite Miss Ruth story regards the incident of the strawberry jam:

Shortly after World War II ended, strawberry jam made its first appearance at Tucker Brothers Groceries in West Fitchburg. This was not some thin wartime paste like we had from the army. Every so often, Dad's friends at Fort Devens would send us a pack of C-Rations. Inside was a sealed pouch of biscuits, which were hard as rocks, and a tin of something that passed for jam. You had to read what was written on the top, as you could never guess what it was from the smell, taste or look of it alone. Dad said, "It probably tastes much better when you're eating it in a foxhole." But this new stuff, the strawberry jams that arrived at Tucker Brothers in the mid-Forties, Ahhhh. It was the real McCoy. It was dark and thick strawberry jam with real whole strawberries in it. It was what the gods ate when they snacked.

We finished off that jar in record time and I pleaded for another. It was not in the family food budget that day, my mother said. Nana, who had enjoyed her share of the jam with her tea, managed to come up with a few coins that she gave me from her little purse. I grabbed my bicycle and headed for Tucker Brothers to buy our second jar of strawberry jam.

When I got to the store, the shelf was empty. The strawberry jam had sold out. I went right to the top: Miss Ruth herself. She was sitting by the cash register with her magazine, as usual, and she listened absently to my report about the empty shelf. "Miss Tucker," I concluded, "the strawberry jam is all sold out."

"It certainly is," she replied emphatically, "and good riddance to it! There will be no more strawberry jam in this store, I can tell you that."

I was puzzled. "Why? Everybody thought it was so good. It's all gone. Please order some more."

"No, I will not," she replied firmly. "I have better things to do with my time than stock shelves with things like strawberry jam that just sell out too fast to little boys with more money than is good for them. I do not need more ways to make work for myself."

The discussion was over and she turned back to her reading. Now, I knew there was something wrong with what she said, but I couldn't quite put my finger on it. I got back on my bicycle and came home. I gave Nana back her money and told her the whole story. "What happened?" I asked her.

Nana chuckled. "It is unseen to her when even a small boy like ye knows there is something wrong with what she said. She was wrong, child. She is there to put things on the shelves, and the more she has to do, the better off they will all be. Ye cannot hold a job and look for ways to be lazy. Miss Ruth has lost sight of why she is there. It would be like the priest sweeping everybody out of church, God forgive me, so he could lock it up early and go home. There are some things that just are not done. It reminds me of my father and his brother and their story of the train that carried the farm produce from Lixnaw to Dublin. Did I ever tell ye about that?

The Dublin Express

"My father's brother Dan worked for the railroad that ran the train to Dublin. It stopped in our village at Lixnaw. I say it stopped, because we had an official station there, but it rarely did. No one from our village would be going to Dublin, and no one from Dublin had any reason to be stopping for us. The train went through once or twice a day and we would go out to see if we could wave at Uncle Dan as the train rattled and rumbled through the village square, but that was the extent of it.

We learned the most about the train when Uncle Dan would come over to visit and tell us his wonderful stories about working on the railroad. 'There is no power like steam,' he would say. 'There's no limit to it at all. When that boilin' steam hits the piston it drives those iron road wheels at any speed you can imagine. There's nothing faster. Those big wheels will turn as fast as ye can shovel in the coal and make the steam pressure that drives them. We'll never see any power to match it in our lifetime, and that's for sure.' My father would nod in agreement and the stories would go on for most of the evening.

Then there were the jokes and the stories about the fights. The jokes were always on the new boys they hired. The crew would send them on a fool's errand. Like telling them to get some red kerosene to fill the red lanterns they hung on the back of the last railway car at night. The new boys would go from crew to crew with all the old timers in on the joke and saying they were out of the red oil themselves. 'Go down the track a way to the next working party and they might have some red kerosene to spare.' The boys would be walking all day before they figured out, or someone told them, the joke. Then they'd come back all sheepish and laugh at their own foolishness and they would be one of the gang, anxious for their turn to play it on the next newcomer.

Ye don't get the joke, child? God keep ye simple. Think about it for a while.

The fights were part of it too. The engineers were the lords of the line and no one dared disobey or challenge them. Their word was law. They were usually big, strong men who had worked their way up to their position after years of hard labor and heavy work. Whenever a new engineer was assigned to a crew he would establish himself on the first day. Often he'd do it by picking a fight with the biggest man on the crew and show he wasn't afraid of a bit of rough and tumble, and could do it if he had to. I don't know if there were any small engineers, or what they did if there were any. The engineers in Uncle Dan's stories were all heroic as he aspired to be one himself. He actually became one several years later.

To get on with it, the problem started when Tom Doyle, the farmer, contacted your Uncle Dan to make arrangements to ship a trainload of his produce to the open-air markets in Dublin. The Doyle farm had a good year and there were so many vegetables available that they figured they could fill one of those railway cars that rumbled through each day. They'd send the vegetables to the city folks in Dublin who had nothing like this fine, fresh food available to them. Tom Doyle would make a fine profit. Your Uncle Dan agreed it was a grand idea and told the local stationmaster to make arrangements for the train to stop at the Lixnaw station to take on the load from the Doyle Farm. Tom himself would ride up with it to Dublin and supervise the entire operation. The stationmaster didn't seem too happy with the idea, but he said nothing Uncle Dan could hear, so everybody thought the deal was done.

Came the big day, and the Doyle farm had several wagons waiting by the station for the train that was to come through at 6:05 in the morning. The mayor, the constable, the priest, and the schoolteacher with her entire class were on hand to see this important event. We all waited patiently for the train.

Shortly after 6AM we felt the rumble on the rails and a bit after that the long pull of the steam whistle as the train chugged its way down the grade and up the little rise that led to Lixnaw. Closer and closer it came, and louder and louder grew the whistle as it approached the station at a high rate of speed. The children all clapped and whooped. Tom Doyle said to Uncle Dan, 'It's going too fast. That train is not about to stop in Lixnaw this day.' And he was right. With another whoop of the whistle and blast of the steam, the little train sped right past the station and continued on up the grade toward Dublin. The crowd was silent.

'And what is this then?' said Tom Doyle to the station master, 'why didn't ye stop the train?'

'I didn't want to slow it down,' the stationmaster said.

'I didn't want ye to slow it down,' said Tom Doyle, getting more angry by the moment, 'I wanted ye to stop it entirely.'

'It already had a load of produce for Dublin,' the stationmaster countered, 'and I didn't want to slow the train down on this grade for that would delay its arrival at the Dublin market.'

Tom Doyle shook his head and turned to Uncle Dan. 'Explain it to him,' he said, 'and tell your employers at the railroad that they owe me for a load of produce that will go bad sitting here by the tracks waiting for the train that comes through tomorrow.'

Uncle Dan put that message on the wire. Within a short time the railroad came back with an answer. They were sending a smaller train along right away. It would pick up the produce in the carriage it would bring with it. They would get everything to Dublin only a few hours later than the original plan. They also had some choice words for the stationmaster. Uncle Dan gave those to him for a private read, so we never knew exactly what they said. We guessed they said that someone would be up to talk with him soon.

And they were as good as their word. The little train came along shortly thereafter. It stopped and took on the load from the Doyle Farm along with Tom himself. The whole lot of it went to Dublin where he sold it off at a fine profit and made arrangements for further sales in the future.

The train stopped in Lixnaw with great frequency after that," Nana said. "Once in a while, one of the people in the village would ride up to Dublin with Tom and help him unload for the pay and the fun of it. For days after that they would go about for tea, from cottage to cottage, telling everyone about the wonders of Dublin. It was a great honor to work the train to Dublin with Tom Doyle. Good man that he was, he brought along as many of the townsmen, and even some of the boys, as he could.

"And what happened to the stationmaster who forgot why he was there?" I asked.

"There was a new station master soon after that," she said, "The other fellow was given a broom and a shovel. His job now was to sweep and clean the platform and load and unload the wagons. It was many years after that before he earned his right to take over the big job as stationmaster once again. And he only got considered for that when Ton Doyle himself gave him a reference.

Tom knew that this time, the station master understood why he was there."

Nana, Enright's Pharmacy, And The Giant In The Stone

My father was a great believer that an idle mind is the devil's workshop. As a result, he found part time jobs for all his children among his many business friends in the city. When I was 14, in 1952, my father got me my first job working for his friend Harold Enright, a druggist who owned and operated Enright's Pharmacy on Main Street. I ran the soda fountain. Today that position might be called "Vice President of Fountain Operations". At the time it was called "Soda Clerk" or less elegantly, "Soda Jerk."

Nana Ware was proud of my entry into the workingman's world and was suitably impressed when I brought home nearly eight dollars in my first pay package. "Seventy-five cents an hour," she marveled, "it's a man's wage."

Enright's was the Main Street watering hole and neighborhood social center. Everyone in town stopped by to deposit and withdraw the latest gossip and other news of the day. Just eavesdropping on this adult chatter, and studying some of the products available for sale, matured me about two years in my first three months of employment.

Harold was a firm but fair boss. He did not believe in teenage idle hands either (the feeling seems to have been epidemic in 1950's Fitchburg) and he kept us moving all the time. If the fountain was slow, you swept floors or washed the windows. There were shipments to be opened and checked in and shelves to be dusted and stocked. You never stood there with your hands swinging while you were on the clock. On the other hand, sometimes when things were quiet, Harold would just sit at the fountain and talk with me about things we felt were important. He had two daughters about my age and was a pretty warm and sensitive guy beneath the gruff exterior he could turn on at the drop of a hat. He never minded the occasional free Coke or sundae for personal consumption. He missed nothing and kept a wary eye on both employees and customers. Once, an older man came in and asked Harold's help in picking out a birthday card for a friend. Harold soon pried out of him that the man could not read. Before he left the store with his card, the man also had an appointment scheduled with a retired special education teacher who lived in one of the apartments over the store. The following Christmas, Harold proudly showed me a holiday card he had received. It had been addressed and signed by the man who the previous summer could not read or write.

The bane of Harold's existence was Mr. Boru, the elderly gentleman who lived in the apartment house next door.

Mr. Boru, like most of the retired people who lived along Main Street, spent the good weather days walking along the "main drag", as we called it, looking in shop windows, visiting the library, and taking in the occasional afternoon movie. He always took his evening meal at Enright's Pharmacy, and it was always the same order: A toasted cheese sandwich and a cup of tea.

This is the part where Harold would come unglued.

According to our menu, a toasted cheese sandwich was twenty-five cents. That bought you a slice of cheese between two buttered pieces of toast. However, buttered toast was ten cents an order by itself, and the menu also offered a slice of cheese "on any fountain order" for an extra ten cents. Every night Mr. Boru would order toast with a side of cheese and pay us twenty cents. That drove Harold crazy.

"That's a toasted cheese sandwich," Harold would tell Mr. Boru. "You owe me twenty-five cents."

"It is not," Mr. Boru would reply, "it's an order of toast with a side of cheese. That's twenty cents."

"But," Harold would press on, "you put the cheese between the pieces of toast and that makes it a sandwich."

"How else would I eat it?" Mr. Boru would say. "And what sort of philosopher are you to define the nature of a sandwich anyway?" And on and on they'd go, with no resolution, and no compromise. It made Harold very upset. I think it made Mr. Boru very happy.

I used to tell Nana these and other stories from the working world, and she loved them. She always had an insight or comment to make along the way. "Harold sometimes thinks like Miss Ruth," she laughed. "He forgets he is there to sell whatever people want to buy. If he can make toast and cheese for twenty cents at a profit, he should lower the sandwich price to twenty cents as well and let Mr. Boru get the better of the deal. Then, maybe Mr. Boru will spend more money there and it will be better for everyone."

One night, I told her an especially good story about Mr. Boru's antic torments of Harold. Harold marked everything in the store with his cost based on a code he had created. My father, the amateur cryptographer, figured out that the code was based on Harold's family name and the ten letters in the phrase, *Buy Enright*. Therefore, the letter "B" = 1, the letter "U" = 2, and so forth. If a product was marked "BNT" it meant it had cost Harold $1.50.

Mr. Boru broke the code. It was the greatest code breaking success since World War II in Bletchley, England when the Allies cracked the German Enigma machine. "Harold," Mr. Boru would call across the store, "If this costs you $1.50 why do I have to pay $3.00 for it? Will you take $2.50?" Harold would turn red, make that strangling sound in his throat that worried us all so much, and rush into the back room to recover. Mr. Boru would chuckle and go back to his twenty-cent supper.

Nana smiled when I told her about this development and said, "Mr. Boru is torturing him now. Harold should graciously give him his twenty cent supper before the old man drives him to an early grave." She paused for a moment that asked, "Do you know that name, Boru?"

"He was an Irish hero," I said. "A king, I think."

"Aye, a king," she said, happy that some of her knowledge had been successfully transferred. "A high king and the greatest of our heroes - both. Do ye know what he did for Ireland?" I said no, I didn't know all about it. And Nana told this story…

The Giant In The Stone

"I have told ye about the haunted forts, and the burial mounds, and the banshee, and the Little People, and even about old Agnes, the Witch of Lixnaw. Now I will tell ye about the Old Ones; the people from before time itself that sleep in the hills awaiting the call to arms.

It was a thousand or more years ago, the Seanchai told us, that the North men came to Ireland. They arrived from God knows where in their long dragon boats. The people hid along the shores and watched them. They wore scarlet cloaks and gleaming helmets of silver and gold that shone in the bright sun. The helmets were crowned with two enormous horns, and they looked like human bulls or oxen. They grew great blonde, almost white, bushy beards and wore shining armor. They carried sharp battle-axes, swords, and spears. They were fearful to see.

They had war trumpets in each dragon boat and they blew long, mournful notes as they plied the waterways, signaling each other as to where they were while terrifying the poor villagers who lived along the shore in their farms and cottages. The people knew they were not prepared for the likes of the North men.

I don't know exactly where they came from. Some said they were two different people - not one. There was an old poem my father used to say. I remember this much of it:
'And ever on they came at us,
Through ocean winds and rains,
The light ones were the Vikings,
And the dark ones were the Danes.'
It was a harsh and cruel time to be poor, but then, isn't it always? The North men were fierce and showed no mercy. They took what they wanted and spared no one in their fury. They would attack all the towns and villages they came upon, take all that was there, and set the rest ablaze with the torch. The lucky villagers were the ones who died in the fighting. The others were taken off to slavery and never seen again. There was no escaping them. The

101

Church even had a special prayer that the people would say at their evening services hoping that the hand of God would intervene on their behalf.

> 'From ghoulies and ghosties,
> and long legged beasties,
> and things that go bump in the night,
> protect us, Oh Lord.
> And from the fury of the North men, deliver us.'

"What were 'beasties"? I asked.

"Beasties were rats," she spat. "Dirty, sickness carrying rats. Now, these North men were very clever. When the people finally got themselves organized and took up arms against them, the North men tried new tricks. They would land their dragon ships along the coast and march noisily inland to take up battle positions before the town's fortifications. Then they would send in an emissary to tell the people that all they wanted was the gold they needed to buy supplies and return home. Give us gold and supplies, they said, and we will be gone before nightfall.

The people, of course, wanted to believe them. They would send out gold and supplies and the North men would accept it all gladly. Then they would tell the people, it's not enough. You insult us. Give us more so we can be gone from this place today. The people would think, 'We are so close; let us give them more and be rid of them.' And they would send out more. The North men would accept it gladly. Then they would say, 'Not quite enough. Send us a bit more and we will be on our way home this very day.' And the people would do it again, and again, until they had stripped the town of everything they had. Then the North men would attack anyway to pillage and plunder the bit that was left, and then kill and burn. Ah, there was no stopping them.

Finally, the people could take it no more. They had to leave their farms and come into the towns where they could look after one another. The fewer farms meant less food, and the people suffered greatly. Then the people turned to one of their own warlords. His name was Brian Boru and he lived in a lavish fortification on the mountain at Tara. He had many warriors around him, along with their families. The people made him High King of Ireland and put all their faith in him to save them from the North men. He then united Ireland under his rule and declared war on the invaders from the North.

Brian Boru was one of Ireland's greatest warriors and heroes. He overcame all the differences among the bands and clans and brought all the Irish warriors into one great army. He struck at the North men wherever they landed and tried to build their camps. They found no easy time of it now. No one listened to their stories, or was taken in by their tricks. Brian Boru and his army struck at them by day and by night, and met fire and sword with fire and sword. Ah, it was a great battle that raged between them.

This was all new to the North men. They had always been on the attack and never the defense. Now someone was attacking them using their own fierce ways. They started to lose both boats and men. The game was no longer worth the candle. The North men began to withdraw from Ireland.

Finally, one day there was a last great battle near Tara that settled the matter forever. King Brian Boru learned that the North men had landed on the shores nearby and built camps to resupply their boats. He attacked them with a great army and drove them from the place. It was an epic battle, and both sides fought fiercely and courageously. But the Irish were fighting for their homeland and that gave them the advantage that turned the day. Gradually, they took command of the battle. By nightfall they had burnt the North men's fortifications and sent those who survived paddling off in the few dragon ships that were left to them.

It was a great victory, but the Irish paid a terrible price for it. King Brian Boru lay mortally wounded on the battlefield.

They bound up the King's wounds and took him to his tent. A special tent he had, for he was a giant of a man, they say. 'Seven feet was his height with some inches to spare,' and he was as round and sturdy as the great oaks that surrounded his castle at Tara.

He lay there all one night and half the next day without change. Then he told his people to prepare a wagon to take him up into the mountains that surrounded the valley where the battle had raged. They did as he said without question. Injured as he was, he was still the King and he supervised the entire march. He directed them to the sheltered side of the mountain that looked out over the valley and the sea.

'This is the place,' said he. 'I can watch over ye all from here. He got up from his litter bed and walked slowly over to the rock wall and touched it with his sword. There was a great rumbling sound and the rock opened up and there was a pathway into the mountain. 'I will rest here,' he said, going inside, 'and I shall sleep and heal and regain my strength. And I will be ready should the North men return. I will hear ye when ye call. And I will come when I am summoned. And the High King of Tara will fight once again for the land and the people he loves.'

And with that, the side of the mountain swung closed behind him and King Brian Boru was at rest, inside the rock, watching over us for all time."

"And did he ever come back?" I asked.

"No," Nana replied, "not for these thousand and more years. He has gathered about him the greatest warriors of the ages since, and they are ready. One day he will return when someone with a pure heart calls him and answers his questions."

"What questions are those?"

"Ye must call his name in the mountains, 'Brian Boru, Brian Boru...' And if ye call him long enough and loud enough, and with a good heart, in its own time the wind will sigh, 'Who is it that ye call?'

And ye must say, 'I call Brian Boru, the Lord of Tara, and High King of all Ireland.'

And the wind will ask, 'What do ye want of Brian Boru?'

And ye must say, 'Ireland has need of him once again.'

And the wind will reply, 'Then he will come.' And the rock will open, and Brian Boru, the Lord of Tara and High King of Ireland, will step forth in all his might and glory to serve his people once more. And there is none to stand up to the likes of him.

God Bless Ireland Forever! Erin Go Bragh!"

Nana, The Sea Serpent, and St. Patrick

The best conversations with Nana were over her afternoon tea break. My mother usually handled all the arrangements, but once in a while she went shopping and when I left St. John's Grammar School at 3:30PM, I arrived home just in time to prepare Nana's afternoon tea and Graham crackers with butter. I had the same snack myself, and we would just sit and talk. It was a great time for both social and serious conversation.

She told me all about tea, including the "thrice brewed tea" of her native Ireland in the 1800's. "Tea was expensive," she said, "and not many outside of the great houses could afford it. The Quality would have their tea every afternoon and the servants, like me, would save the grounds and later brew tea for us and the people who worked downstairs. That was the second brewing. Then, they would give the grounds to friends and family, or sell them at the back door for a penny. Now the tea grounds would be brewed a third time for the poor. This was 'thrice brewed tea'."

Once in the early Forties, Aunt Fanny, who was married to Uncle George, came to have tea with Nana. Aunt Fanny offered to brew the tea herself. Tea bags were new and she had never seen them before. She had used only the bulk tealeaves that come in the large cans people would keep ready in their pantries. She took forever to brew the tea. When she finally brought it to Nana, she said, "I don't know why Kathryn can't buy tea in those one pound cans like the rest of us. It takes forever to rip open all those little bags to get enough to

105

brew a pot full." Nana nearly fell out of her chair laughing at the thought of it.

One day, Nana and I were talking about what was going on in my life. I told her that a school friend of mine, a little girl named Janice, had been struck by lightning and killed. It had bothered me a lot. I thought of her as being far away from her family now, and all alone. That was a sad thought.

"But that's not the way of it," said Nana. "Did ye n'eer hear of St. Patrick's promise?" I said I had not, and Nana told this story.

The Snake, The Sea Serpent, and St. Patrick

"It was a thousand or more years ago when St. Patrick came to Ireland and brought us the Faith. He preached the message of the Trinity with the shamrock that had three leaves yet one flower. He converted the pagans, and drove all the snakes out of Ireland. St. Patrick could not abide a serpent. It was one such that had caused us to be driven out of the Garden of Eden. St. Patrick knew that all the world's trouble stemmed from that one evil snake.

So, St. Patrick went among the highways and byways of Ireland, hills and valleys alike, singing his special song. It was a song no serpent could resist. They came out of the woods and the rocks and followed him into the sea as he rowed out in his boat. And they were never heard from again.

All the snakes were gone, but one. This snake had found a hole so deep that no sound could reach him. He hid there until St. Patrick had passed him by and all the other snakes had gone to their fate. And then he stayed there a while more. And then a little while beyond that. And then he slithered back up the hole onto the surface of the land, where he found himself the only snake in Ireland.

Now he hadn't been back more than a little while when he saw a child picking berries on the hill and singing a glad song. 'Why should that child be happy when I am not?' the snake thought to himself. He hid in the brush and watched and listened to her song, growing more jealous and angrier by the moment. He let the child came nearer, nearer, and then he struck! He sunk his fangs deep into the child's leg and she fell down and went into a deep sleep with the poison.

Soon, he heard a man calling out her name. 'Molly? Molly, dear. Where are ye, child?' It was her father, and the snake, coward that he was, hid himself in the brush once again. 'Molly? What has happened, child? Why don't ye answer me?' the father said. Then he saw her lying on the hillside and he came over to her. 'Good God help us', he said, as he stood over her and saw the marks on her little leg. 'She is dead of the serpent's poison.' And with tears and great sorrow, he picked her up and carried her a full day's walk across the bogs and into the hills where St. Patrick lived in his monastery and preached to the people. 'There is a serpent left among us,' the man said, as he set the child's body down at the great saint's feet and asked for his help and intercession.

Saint Patrick looked at the young girl's body and bade the father move her to a soft bed of greens and hay. He had one of the women rub the child's leg with a mixture of herbs and roots that she had gathered from the woods. Then they all knelt and prayed together for the rest of that long night. And a very long night it was. Once, at midnight, the child cried out. They renewed their prayerful efforts with much gratitude for this sign. By morning the child was awake and on the way to a full recovery."

"And what happened to the snake?" I asked.

"St. Patrick himself went into the hills and drove the serpent out of his hiding place. The snake begged for mercy but Patrick said there were little mercy in Heaven and none on earth for anyone who harms a child with evil intent. Jesus himself said it was better for such a one to have a millstone tied about his neck and cast into the deepest pit in the sea. And that is what St. Patrick did with the evil serpent. He drove the snake before him to the deepest lake in the mountains and laid on it the three curses of the damned."

"And what are they?" I asked, spellbound.

"The first was that it grows in size and be forever consumed with hunger. In that way it would spend its days and nights in search of food with no time to harm anyone, let alone a child.

The second was that it become afraid of mankind and waste its years in hiding away from any contact with our kind.

And third, the worst of all was that it lives forever and ever in this lonely way until the end of time.

And the serpent is still there in one of those deep lakes," she said, "hiding by day and feeding by night, and wishing for an end to its tormented existence."

"So the child got well, and the serpent was condemned to the lake. But, what was the promise of St. Patrick you mentioned?" I asked.

"St. Patrick told the child's father that our departed loved ones never feel alone, for time passes differently in Heaven then it does here on earth. Why, ye arrive in Heaven early on a day and there are all your family and loved ones, come to welcome ye and find out what ye have been doing since they saw ye last. Ye all tell great stories about old times long past—and there's laughter and perhaps a few tears of joy.

Then, later in the day, come all your friends and the people from the village to welcome and renew the old acquaintance. And that's another great gathering that seems to take but a bit of time it passes so quickly.

But then, they say it could be two score years or more that have passed down here. And along come all the loved ones ye thought were left behind. Sure, didn't ye just see then a few short hours ago? And it's yourself that's greeting them in love and friendship for being reunited once again, and hearing them tell the stories of long times since.

The Lord and St. Patrick take care of their own," she said, nodding gently. "The promise of St. Patrick is that for the Faithful, the dead are never alone. Everyone has someone who cares to love and look after them. And we will all meet again - soon enough—in a better world than this."

Nana, Aunt Fanny, and Life In The Mills

If you lived in Fitchburg during the first half of the 20th
Century, chances were good that you worked in one of the many
paper mills that supported the local economy. There were other
employers in town to be sure, and many independent business people
just as today, but the overwhelming majority of workers reported each
day to one of the several paper mills dotting the city landscape and
belonging to either Crocker-Burbank or Fitchburg Paper Company.
As far back as I can remember, these mills ran three shifts a day,
seven days a week, paid a fair wage, and made overtime available on
a regular basis.

The mills owned several neat and well-maintained houses
throughout the city. As your career advanced, and you rose in the
seniority ranks, you could apply to live in a company home in the
neighborhood of your work, at a substantially reduced rent. The
house was even maintained by company personnel. The only
downside was that if you lost your job, you lost your housing too.
That could be quite a bit to absorb in a short period of time.
However, the mill managers were fair about it and I never heard any
horror stories about people being turned out into the streets. I never
saw any arrangement quite like it until years later when I went into
the army and found that was how military post commanders and their
key staff people lived as well. In both cases, it was good duty.

The quality of life in the mills during Nana's time, however,
was a different matter altogether. One of my father's friends said at

109

our dinner table one night that the only reason the Chinese weren't enslaved by the railroads, and the mills didn't enslave the Irish, was that the owners learned that slavery was too expensive. You had to take some care of your own property, he said. It was much cheaper to give the later minorities a subsistence wage. Then let them be worked by the foreman as a replaceable resource, and gouged by the company store. The end of slavery was as much a business decision as it was a moral triumph.

Nana's husband George, my grandfather, worked in those mills as a teamster in the latter years of the 19th Century. His son, my Uncle George, worked in those same mills in the slightly more enlightened days around World War I. So did Uncle George's wife, Aunt Fanny. Thereby hangs this tale.

When Uncle George asked Aunt Fanny to marry him in the spring of 1910, he had just mustered out of the army after the clean-up following the Spanish-American War. The soldiers knew that this conflict had been a dress rehearsal and that something big was coming. The Great War in Europe was already on their horizon. Uncle George knew he would be recalled to active service. Both he and Aunt Fanny realized how difficult marital separations could be. They agreed to postpone their marriage until more peaceful times. And postpone it they did. They were finally married thirty-nine years later, in 1949. Uncle George was not one to rush into things. It is just as well that they waited until after World War I, but they waited until after World War II as well. It is a good thing that Uncle George did not sense the Korean Conflict looming ahead in the Fifties, as the wedding delays might have continued through all the wars we have fought since 1910.

They had fifteen years together, and then Uncle George died and Aunt Fanny was on her own once again. I remember the last time I saw Uncle George. He was in a nursing home in the city. He would call and ask my mother to send down one of the boys to shave him. Uncle George was a great admirer of women, but he firmly believed that only a man could properly shave another man. I must have qualified because I was sent down there from time-to-time and did my part. Unfortunately for Uncle George, a well-intentioned, left-handed teenager wielding a razor while shaving another man was not as danger free as he might have hoped. I frequently nicked him here and there, but except for the occasional dry comment ("Cut off the other ear, why don't you, so that both sides of my head will match."), he was most patient and appreciative.

In 1959, I graduated from the University of Massachusetts at Amherst and earned both my degree and an ROTC commission as a Second Lieutenant in the US Army Reserve. My fiancée Judy and I were getting married two weeks later. I had a job of sorts working as a janitor at Burbank Hospital for the summer and parking cars nights at Bill Mallahy's Funeral Home. We were going to Ft. Knox, Kentucky in early September for AOB as the army called it, Armored Officers' Basic. It was a heady time for a twenty-one year old with a college degree, a gold bar, and a beautiful young bride.

Uncle George had seen my older cousins, the Beauvais brothers, in uniform during World War II. They all saw action across Europe and accounted for themselves with both dignity and bravery. Now, Uncle George wanted to see the next family generation in uniform. When I arrived home from school, I put on my dress greens, with the gold bar so brightly buffed it would blind you, and went to visit Uncle George in the nursing home. He was genuinely pleased and talked to me as man-to-man, soldier-to-soldier. The only time he laughed was when he asked if I was Regular Army and I told him, "No, Uncle George, I am R.F.A."

"What the hell is R.F.A?"

"The army says it stands for "Reserve Forces Act," but the sergeants say it stands for "Russia's Future Allies.""

He laughed, hugged me, and proudly introduced me to his friends. We just sat there for a while. He was a big man even in old age and he closed his larger hand over mine for a while. His eyes misted up and I think he was back in a place where he could only go alone. Finally, he asked, "How long does it take to make First Lieutenant?" I told him it took eighteen months. "Then I still outrank you," he said, "you made me very happy. Go home now." I left and never saw him alive again.

After Uncle George died, Aunt Fanny continued to work at the mill, just as she done for those "few years" in the middle of their courtship. She was a strong and fiercely independent woman.

In 1912, she had taken a job in the laboratory of the Fitchburg Paper Company, testing paper samples for the correct chemical formulation. She kept this same job for sixty-two years, and I mean the identical job. And she did it into the early Seventies just as she had done it in 1915. My brother Leo, the management consultant, said that Aunt Fanny's career advancement was yet another testimonial to our family's meteoric rise up through the ranks of American Industry.

However, Aunt Fanny was happy at her work-a-day job and totally oblivious to the wheels of big business clanking away behind the scenes. She knew little about the mergers and acquisition binge that US industry was about to launch during the Sixties and Seventies.

One day, all employees were notified that giant Krypton Industries had acquired the stock and the assets of Fitchburg Paper, along with Aunt Fanny and her long-term job in the laboratory. She had no idea of the ramifications of a merger but, as always, she figured if she kept her head down and did her job that "this too shall pass."

And, for the most part, she was right. However, about six months after the acquisition, the personnel manager of Krypton Industries called his now subordinate personnel manager at Fitchburg Paper, and tweaked him about a funny error they had found in the latter's personnel files.

"If these records are correct," chuckled the big guy, "you have a woman working in the laboratory who has been there, in the very same job, for nearly sixty-three years! Ha, ha, ha…"

"Oh, that's Fanny," said the local personnel guy. "She does a good job and seems quite happy there."

The headquarters man was horrified. "You mean there really is somebody like that?" cried the big guy, "An old woman? She has been there for sixty-three years? Are you mad? She's a liability! Put her on pension or something. Just get rid of her…today!"

It made no sense for the local guy to argue with the headman. He was a headquarters type and facts just seemed to confuse him. The Fitchburg Paper personnel manager followed orders and drafted up a retirement package. Then he called in Aunt Fanny to discuss the change. He told her it was retirement time. Today.

"Is that my personnel jacket?" Aunt Fanny asked.

"Yes, it is."

"Hmmmm. Then it must have all my performance information. Tell me, how many tardys have I had? Unauthorized sick days? Warnings? Disciplinary actions of any kind?"

"Why," said the personnel manager, thumbing feverishly through the file, "I see none. Nothing negative at all."

"Oh good. And my performance appraisals, how have they been?"

"They've all been…Excellent…to Outstanding."

"Yes. I've been "Employee of the Year" several times. Is all that in there?"

"Yes, that's all in here too."

"Fine. I think I'm entitled to a copy of that whole file. Is that so?"

"Yes, that's legally your right," said the personnel manager, now sensing something about to snap shut, probably around his neck, "but why would you want it?"

"Oh," Aunt Fanny replied, "I've been reading about all these new women's groups, and what they've been doing for elderly women like me. Women with perfect work records. Good performance appraisals. Women who are losing their jobs for no good reason. I bet," Aunt Fanny chuckled her favorite chuckle, "I bet that I'll be the first Spanish-American War *and* World War I widow they ever had to represent!"

The personnel manager turned white. His left eye started to twitch. He felt his whole career leaking away through the balls of his feet. "Fanny," he mumbled, "would you mind waiting here a few minutes while I go make an important call?"

"Not at all." Aunt Fanny smiled graciously.

The personnel manager was instantly on the phone with his new boss, telling him what had transpired. "Spanish-American War *and* World War I widow"…"Thrown out"…"Women's groups!" It just got worse and worse.

"Good Lord!" said the corporate guy. "It will be in all the papers! On TV! Our major shareholders are rich old widows. They'll turn on us. The papers will demand an investigation! And women's groups? They'll be burning their underwear in front of the executive building! Management will need a goat! I'll be held responsible! I'm dead! Everything will be gone. Give that crazy old woman whatever she wants! Get a liability release! You've gotten us into this mess; now solve the problem, today!" He slammed down the phone.

The local personnel guy took a few minutes to calm down. He knew the preliminaries were over. He was playing for keeps. He came back to Aunt Fanny with one of his best smiles. "An honest question, Fanny," he said. "What would it take for you to just go home quietly…and stay there? An improved pension package, perhaps?"

"Oh," said Aunt Fanny, "these pensions and benefit packages confuse me. Make it simple: Just continue my pay, insurance, and benefits package just as though I still worked here. Then I'll go away quietly. I will also look forward to the wonderful party I'm sure you'll have for me and my friends in the company recreation center next door."

"Done!"

And so it was that Aunt Fanny spent the rest of her days on full salary and benefits. She never set foot inside Fitchburg Paper again, except for the lovely party they threw for her family and friends. She later confided to us that she didn't miss it that much anyway. "It was just a job," she said. Besides, within a month, she had another full time position, working for the local shoppers' newspaper. She stuffed in the weekend advertising supplements. She found it challenging work, and Aunt Fanny always went for the cutting edge positions. In fact, if she hadn't passed on many years later, she might be working there yet.

Nana Ware wasn't with us to hear the end of this story, but it was the kind of story she loved. The mills were never far from her mind, and her memories were not gentle like mine. Her memories were of a harder time. Her life, like the lives of all her friends and neighbors, revolved around what happened in the mills. And the stories she would tell when the family gathered around her were about what went on in the mills: The dangers, the indignities, and the pettiness.

"God help ye if ye got injured in the mills," she said. There were few safety devices and no insurance to provide a bit of help for the families. "If ye were injured and still able to work, the boss might let ye have a light job like night watchman. That was how they took care of the injured and crippled, and it was grateful ye were for the job."

I remember one story she told about a young laborer who came to work one day after Christmas wearing a bright new tie. He was fired at once by a foreman who told him, "I won't have a common laborer dressing like a boss."

Some of the mills were owned and managed by extended family members of the founders. Like any family business, that meant you had some good people and some bad people. Unfortunately, the bad ones had as much influence and family protection as the good ones. I started collecting anecdotes about one young mill boss they talked about. I call him "Happy Happenstance." He was a playboy to his fair weather friends, a boor to people of his social level, and a terror to the poor and powerless who worked for him. He was hateful to work for. The story of his career was told many times by Nana and the other family members who were among the hundreds who worked for him. Years later, I put all I remembered into a story poem that went like this:

Happy Happenstance II (R.I.P)

Headline, Fitchburg Sentinel:
LOCAL INDUSTRIALIST DEAD AT 87
H. ("HAPPY") Happenstance Collapses at Golf Club
Gifts To City Include Civic Parks
Eulogies Pour In

"Ye speak well of the dead,"
My grandmother said,
"And don't take away from his glory!"

But these people who mourn,
Hadn't even been born,

115

They deserve to know more of his story…

"Happy" Happenstance II
1880 - 1967

It was Nineteen Fifteen, and your chances were lean,
If you worked in the Happenstance Mills.
For ten bucks a week, maybe twelve at your peak,
You could mop up the leaks and the spills.

You worked sixty hours, no time to smell flowers,
Don't ever be late or get sick.
You stay out a day and it's docked from your pay,
And you could get discharged just as quick.

It was damp as old Venice, machines were a menace,
And safety was slender and slight.
So if you lost an arm, it was back to the farm,
Or a job as a watchman by night.

Men took their vacations in payday libations,
And worried each night about bills.
There was family and love and Good God up above,
But He never set foot in the mills.

And if you took a chance, made a move to advance,
You'd likely be left in the lurch.
For in every case, they'd promote the "right" race,
Political party and church.

But "Happy", of course, chased the fox on his horse,
Kept a Duesenberg well stocked with booze.
He rented a villa, a girl named Priscilla,
And later came to on a cruise.

He joked by the rails with the old Prince of Wales,
As the Cunard Line steamed them across.

He returned tanned and tired and had a man fired,
For wearing a tie like a boss.

A few did retire, and move from the fire,
To rocker, to kitchen, to bed.
They dreamed of old friends who had met bitter ends,
And by sixty were burnt out or dead.

It was quite a poor life, filled with longing and strife,
No valleys, just hundreds of hills.
For foul, smelly air and the draught of despair,
Was the lot of the men in the mills.

"Wait! Don't stop there, my son, for a story's not done,
Until Goodness and Virtue succeed!
What came of the bosses, who fashioned those crosses,
Through ignorance, bias, and greed?"
"Did they all bear the cost of the souls that were lost,
Through a lifetime of labor and cares?"
No! Nothing so weighty, they all lived passed eighty,
And passed riches on to their heirs.
For as "Happy" grew old, the Happenstance gold,
Went to libraries, playgrounds, and schools.
They made nice impressions, and took tax concessions,
And well, they had never been fools.

Now his great-grandson prays, we return to the days,
"...Of Integrity, Honor, and Will."
He'd bring us in stages, back to the Dark Ages,
And he'd have the house on the hill.

Yes, "Happy's" a goner, the old prima donna,
He went out still playing his part.
I won't waste my grief on the wicked old thief,
They should put a stake through his heart.

I'd like to believe that we're not so naive,

117

To sell history right down the creek.
But without strict controls, on such self-centered souls,
The bastards would rise in a week.

Nana, Uncle Jim, And The Mermaid

There was a never-ending parade of people through the white house on Temple Street during the 1940's. Many of them were friends and family stopping by to visit Nana Ware. My mother had a whole bevy of friends who would come to visit with her, play Bridge, and chat with Nana, who was a mother figure to them all. The four of us children had playmates and friends in and out of the house all the time. Then there were the uncles, aunts, and of course, the older cousins whom we adored as role models and heroes.

We had a distant cousin from Buffalo named Eddy McManus. He was in the Navy and stationed at Newport, Rhode Island. Every weekend he would come to visit and report to my father what was happening on the war front. It was important to Dad that he get this information first-hand from a family insider. How much of the war Eddy saw from Newport, Rhode Island was always a question mark in some minds.

Eddy would play with us kids, and he was great company. He never lost his temper even when Penny, the family Irish Setter, drooled on his starched, Navy whites.

My cousin Jack Beauvais was also in the Navy aboard ship off somewhere in the Pacific. He would come to see Nana whenever he had home leave. Once both Eddy and Jack were there at the same time. I don't know if they just felt playful, or if I had been unusually annoying, but they decided to play medicine ball - with me as the ball. They had me curl up and hold my knees and then Jack picked me up and threw me to Eddy. Eddy caught me on the fly, bounced me around a few times to find his balance, and then threw me back to Jack. The game went on for several minutes with me sailing through the air until they called it quits. My mother was sure they were going to drop and kill me. My brothers thought that was a risk the family could afford to take. Nana laughed and said, "Leave the boy alone. He'll remember this day for a lifetime." As usual, she was right.

One of the most memorable characters that traipsed in and out of our lives and home was Uncle Jim McQuistan. He had a profound influence on my developing sense of humor and how I look at life that has lasted to this day.

Uncle Jim was not my real uncle. He was another distant cousin. However, he was my father's age and Dad had so few surviving relatives that we could afford to treat Jim as a member of the immediate family.

Jim was well over 6 feet tall and weighed some 300 pounds. He was a hard driving salesman with a taste for good food, good Scotch, and long Cuban cigars. He made his money in sales during the Thirties and Forties, and knew how to get your attention. People would hear his booming voice long before they saw him, and then he would enter and literally fill the room with his girth and his laughter. Think of NBC's Willard Scott in his prime and you have Uncle Jim. It was his humor and good will that won people over. He was the funniest man I ever knew.

I was seven when my mother ushered me to the baby grand piano in Uncle Jim's fine Waltham parlor, and announced I would play my first piano solo. "What's that called, boy?" Uncle Jim asked when I finished. "Swans on the Lake", I replied. "I hope they all drown," he roared. That was just how I felt. He broke me up and I was a fan forever.

He would come to our home for Sunday dinner and take over the conversation with his comments and stories. More often then not, he was the butt of his own jokes. He claimed he went into a leather store to buy a belt and the clerk said, "Sorry, sir, we make for the jockeys, but not for the horses."

Actually, he was an avid horseback rider once he found a horse big enough to carry him. "I ride for the exercise," he

120

announced. He knew the family would say that horseback riding was not much exercise. "It is for my horse!" he'd roar.

Another time he complained that horseback riding was too exhausting. "How can sitting on a horse be exhausting?" my father asked. "Oh?" said Jim. I'm supposed to ride on HIM?"

Long before people sent out photographic Christmas cards, Jim sent us one of himself, all duded out in riding costume, sitting astride a huge Clydesdale. On the bottom he had written, "Uncle Jim on horseback. The one on the bottom is the horse."

Whether his jokes were spontaneous or rehearsed, he had a line for every occasion, and they were priceless. Sometimes he'd play on my father, the family sober sides. Once when Dad declined another of his invitations to go out and have a good time, Uncle Jim said to my mother, "Why don't you bury him and get a live one?" My father was not amused and that just added to the fun.

You could find Uncle Jim at any family gathering surrounded by kids listening to his stories and reveling in his antics. He couldn't just leave a room, for example. He'd grab his collar with one hand, the seat of his pants with the other, and give himself the bum's rush out the door. Nothing got by him unobserved. Once, one of my cousins showed him her new engagement ring. "Lovely," he said, pretending to examine it with an imaginary loupe, "and only the tiniest of flaws in the right oblique facet." How long had he been sitting on that one?

He loved sharing literate puns with people who could field them. Once we ate in a deli and he made a show of counting the Montechristo sandwiches. "There are seven," he whispered to me, "That must be the Count of Montechristo's!"

I had to go to the library and look that one up, but it was worth it.

Being a salesman, he ate out often and had a vast collection of restaurant jokes that I still use to this day. Once he told a waiter who served him a very small steak, "Yes, that's what I want. Bring me some."

Another time he tasted the house white wine and gravely informed the steward, "I'm afraid your horse has diabetes."

121

Or he would order the wine by calling out, "A bottle of your best cheap wine!"

He even memorized things to say about wine, as he tasted it. "An amusing little vintage," he'd snort. "Still, I'm impressed with its pretensions." It didn't mean anything, but only people in on the joke knew that. He would look at a menu and make up something like, "I'll have the pâté de fois plastique with croutons and heavy cream." The waiter would stare at the sandwich menu trying to find that between the hot dogs and the club sandwiches.

He even told my father, in one of those rare instances when Jim didn't grab the bill, "Leave a big tip, I hate to look cheap."

Humor pervaded his life and he was welcomed wherever he went. Uncle Jim's humor was mostly self-directed, or about pretense, or the perversity of inanimate objects. He never hurt anyone. Humor was his buffer against the real world, and the way in which he sold, communicated, and taught. When my brother George bought his first car, Uncle Jim examined it for him and made a number of helpful observations: "Those tires are so thin I can see the air." "Winter's coming on, better put down the earlaps on the distributor cap." "Buckle on the fan belt looks loose, better tighten it up." Pointing to the air filter he asked me, "Do you know how the air gets from there all the way down to the tires?" His final judgment was the best of all: "Your best bet is to jack up the radiator cap and drive a new car under it."

Uncle Jim had great adventures wherever he went. As Oscar Wilde wrote, "He lived a life filled with incident." Actually, I learned that almost everybody has a few great adventures at one time or another, or at least hears great stories from other people who have great adventures. The real difference is that the Uncle Jims of the world better remember those stories and, more importantly, tell them better. Well, that's what I've always tried to do.

I remember one Sunday evening dinner during World War II. My father was talking about the importance of common sense, and Uncle Jim told us how he went to Washington, D.C. on business with a colleague. The fellow he traveled with could have been a great salesman but, as Uncle Jim said, "He talked himself out of too many orders. He never knew when to shut up, and he had bad judgment.

Here's an example of that bad judgment and how it could have gotten us killed:

"We were driving through D.C. when we heard sirens coming up fast from behind us. I was driving, so I pulled over into the breakdown lane and this convoy of big, black 1941 Cadillac limos flying the US flag on their fenders roared by us at high speed. The last vehicle in the convoy was an open army Jeep. In the back were two young Marines manning a tripod mounted .30-caliber machine gun. There was a sign on the Jeep that read, '**Presidential Convoy. Do Not Pass.**' It was Roosevelt, and he was going someplace in a hurry. My colleague said, 'They have no call to do that! This is America and we have rights. Catch up with them and pass that Jeep. We'll show them!'

"I said, 'You damn fool! That's President Roosevelt! Worse yet, it's two young Marines who have been told it's their skin if anything happens to the President. Some sergeant probably said, 'Shoot first and ask questions later.' Edward," he said talking directly to me, "Remember: it doesn't do you a damn bit of good to be right if the other guy has a machine gun."

I told Nana this story later that night. She thought his language may have been rough for someone my age, but his point was a good one. "We all have rights and privileges in this great country," she said, "but there's no sense being a fool about it, is there?"

Nana Ware admired Uncle Jim. For one thing, she could understand him. No person who was hard of hearing ever had to ask, "What did Jim say?" You could hear him across the street. For another, I think she recognized a kindred spirit and respected what she said was a rare gift, "the ability to be an adult among adults, and a child among children." Like herself, he was all that too.

Nana was deeply religious and spent much of her time in prayer and meditation with her beads and prayers and religious radio programs. Once Uncle Jim walked in to say hello and found her with her packet of medals and scapulars on her lap, while she said her beads in front of her little radio table that was covered with statues and holy pictures. "Tell me, Mrs. Ware," he boomed, "Do you believe in God?" Even Nana had to laugh at that bit of irreverence.

123

The Nana In The Chair, And the tales she told
An anecdotal biography of Mary Dunne Ware (1860-1956)

When the McQuistans finally left after dinner, my mother
would say, "I need a quiet time." She might go to her room for a
while or walk up the hill to Sacred Heart Church for a short visit.
She'd take the dimes she had put on top of the china closet and light
votive candles for her special intentions. Dad would disappear into
his Sunday paper. I might sit with Nana and review the stories of the
day. "My father thinks Uncle Jim's jokes are old," I said once.

Nana would smile and nod and say, "That may be true, but he
tells them so well, ye laugh anyway. Besides, no matter how old a
story is, if ye never heard it before it is good as new."

"I wish I could tell stories like Uncle Jim," I'd say.

If wishes were horses, beggars would ride," she'd laugh,
"Perhaps someday you'll be telling the stories like your Uncle Jim,
but like the fisherman and the mermaid, don't waste your wishes on
things ye can get by working for it." And then she told this story:

The Fisherman And The Mermaid

"There was a fisherman we knew when I was a child and his
name was Tim. He was a hard working man but he had a large family
and there was never quite enough money to go around. His wife Nora
was after him by day and night to bring home more money so they
could do a few of the extra things that the other people in the village
did from time to time. Alas, try as he would, Tim never figured out a
way to get the extra money.

In fact, the only thing he owned of value was a set of coral
hair combs that his mother had left him years before. Nora had taken
ownership of those. Handsome combs they were, and fashioned of
rich colored coral. When she wore them to church on Sundays and
Holy Days, she turned many a woman's head. The other women
wished they could festoon themselves in such rich and beautiful
combs. They were both Nora's pride and a source of great comfort to
her.

One day, Tim was down on the shore mending his nets and
thinking about his problems - when he heard a beautiful voice singing
a plaintive song. It was so beautiful; he just sat and listened for a
while. He had to know who could sing such a beautiful song, so he

124

put his nets aside and followed the song down into the large rocks that had settled around the shoreline. The song was coming from the other side of the last huge rock, and Tim peeked around it to see what he could see. It was a mermaid, or a merrow as they call them in that part of Ireland. Beautiful she was, with long dark hair, and a voice like an angel. Now that he was closer, Tim could hear her song:

'My joy is my hair, my long, beautiful hair,
Which I'd fashion with combs made of coral.
My heart to the man, and good fess to his clan,
Who brings me fine combs made of coral.'

And now Tim could see that beautiful as she was, and as glorious as was her hair, she had no combs with which to secure it. In that moment, Tim knew what he must do.

Off he went to his cottage near the shore, and took his wife Nora's grandest possession, the coral combs. Back he ran to the beach and the rocks hoping the mermaid would still be there, singing her song on the rock. As he grew closer, he heard the beautiful sound once again, and he knew he was in time.

'Excuse me, your ladyship,' he said, stepping gently from behind the rock so as not to frighten her. 'I heard your song and I have brought you these glorious coral combs for your wonderful long hair.' He held them out for her to see.

The mermaid seemed unsure, and for a moment there he was afraid she would dive back into the sea and be gone from him forever. Then, her eyes moved onto the coral combs, and she smiled. He could tell she agreed they were the finest combs she had ever seen.

'And what is it ye want of me in return?' she asked. 'Am I to be your wife then?'

'No thank you, your ladyship,' Tim said, 'but I have the one wife already and one wife is a splendid sufficiency. But I believe your ladyship has the power of granting wishes, and I ask ye respectfully for the three wishes ye can grant.'

'They are splendid coral combs,' the mermaid said, 'and I will have them. In return, ye may have the three wishes. What would ye have?'

Tim smiled, "A lantern."

'A lantern?' the mermaid asked.

'Aye, a fine lantern like they have on the big boats in Cork. Then I can fish all day and by night too and can bring home the catch I need to support my wife and family.'

The mermaid smiled, 'It is a reasonable enough request,' and - Poof! - Tim held in his hand the finest lantern he had ever seen anywhere in the village.

'And now, he said, 'for my second wish…'

'That is enough for now,' the mermaid said. 'Go home and tell your good wife what has happened and see how she would use your remaining two wishes. Ye are not greedy, Tim, but ye are not wise either. She shall share in your wishes'

And with that, and the coral combs that were his wife's and his mother's before her, the mermaid was gone into the sea.

And so Tim danced up the pathway to his house and sang as he went about in his joy. Nora met him at the door and said, 'Why all the noise and disturbance about you - and where did you get such a fine lantern as that? We could never afford such a thing and ye must take it back where ever ye got it while there is still time.'

And Tim told Nora his story about the song, the mermaid, the combs, the three wishes, and the lantern. When he finally finished, his wife was quiet in her thinking for a long time.

'And my combs are gone then? My beautiful coral combs are gone?'

'Aye,' said Tim, 'but sure we can wish for another set even finer, and we'll get it too. Just as I wished for and got this fine lantern.' And again he showed her his great prize.

'A lantern?' she said. 'Ye wasted a wish on a lantern? Ye could have wished for a ship, or a fine new home, or great wealth and ye wished for a lantern? What a foolish man ye are, Tim! And your foolish lantern be with ye. I wish that lantern was hanging from the end of your nose!'

And with that, Poof! The lantern was hanging from the tip of Tim's nose. He danced around the cottage crying, 'Get it off! Get it off! Get the lantern off me nose!' And of course, Nora realized her mistake, and was sad for it. She used the third wish to take the lantern off her husband's nose. 'I wish the lantern was gone!' she cried, and gone it was."

126

"They had used up the three wishes and had nothing to show for it," I said.

"Worse even," Nana replied, "the beautiful coral combs were gone too, along with the three wasted wishes."

"They must have been very sad," I said.

"For a while," said Nana, "then Tim remembered what the mermaid said about his not being greedy but not wise either. He understood what she meant now. He and Nora talked about these things and tried to find ways to solve their problems by understanding and by working with, and not against, each other. It took a while longer, but Tim and Nora found themselves in a happy marriage and a comfortable life with their family.

"Sometimes, they learned as do we all, that ye have to be careful about what ye wish for. Ye may be worse off if ye get it than ye were when you longed for it. Wishes are the stuff of dreams, but most times, it's just easier to work for what you want," Nana said.

Nana, The Altar Boys, and The Magic Lamp

The big payoff for being an altar boy at Sacred Heart Church in the Forties was our annual trip to the circus. Every June, the Biloxi Brothers Traveling Circus and Tent Show set up on the Falulah Fair Grounds for a week of excitement and adventure for everyone in town who could afford the 25 cents price of admission.

Also on an annual basis, the pastors of the city's several Catholic churches would get together and sponsor a special showing just for their loyal and faithful altar boys. These were the kids who showed up to serve Mass every morning when they were supposed to according to the weekly schedule. Once again, as Nana would say, it was all about showing up, on time, and doing the job.

The special performance of The Biloxi Brothers Traveling Circus for the altar boys was usually on a morning when the circus was not otherwise in operation. This meant a reduced rate for the church and extra income for the circus. It worked out to every one's advantage, particularly the hundred and more altar boys who would show up to be amazed and entertained by the Brothers Biloxi. Our host for this important annual event was our pastor, Father John Mary Flynn, Pastor of Sacred Heart Church. This was a man you did not cross. He was the same priest who once told an annoying bunch of frequent penitents not to worry about going to Confession each and every week, as they probably didn't have the intelligence to commit a mortal sin anyway. However, that is a story for another day.

Actually, it's such a good story that I'll tell it to you when I finish this story about the circus and the magic lamp.

We altar boys began our circus adventure by boarding a rented school bus. It was the first and only time that many of us ever rode a school bus. Part of that was because we lived close to our schools and walked. Part of it was because the city would not provide taxpayer-funded transportation for parochial school kids. "PRCW" we used to say: "Protestants Ride, Catholics Walk."

This particular June morning was the start of a beautiful spring day. We boarded the bus and received the box lunches generously donated by Kendall Catering. The box included lunch, usually a tuna fish or cheese sandwich, and two snacks. This saved the parish money and precluded any embarrassing incident - like last year when one of our boys forgetfully ordered a hot dog on a Friday. He actually ate half of it before Fr. Flynn could get a strangle hold on the boy's neck thus blocking the contaminating swallow and preserving the innocence and integrity of his soul. We all agreed to remind each other not to eat a hot dog on Friday in front of Father Flynn.

We arrived at the fairground to the sound of calliope music coming from the midway. Naturally, the priests had pre-screened the midway to make sure that all risqué and suggestive signs and exhibits had been spirited away into storage. They made sure that ladies in skimpy costumes and the like did not scandalize us. However, there was a strong man and a sideshow. We could throw softballs at weighted milk bottles that never seemed to fall over, have our weight guessed by a midway barker who was always right (it was years before I realized we were all about the same size anyway), and shoot .22 rifles to win any prize on the top shelf by blowing away three stars on a paper target. The stars were about the same size as the .22 bullets we were firing. It was great fun, nobody ever won anything, but it just built up to the Big Top show. The show was wonderful. First, we saw the flags waving in front of a huge tent. Then we heard the barker's voice: "Hurry! Hurry! Hurry! To the biggest little show on the midway. You'll see acrobats and clowns, and trapeze artists and more than even I can tell. It's a treat for children of all ages. The admission is just 25 cents, one quarter of a dollar. You get your money's worth in the first 15 minutes and the rest of the show is free. Hurry, Hurry, Hurry!"

We had heard that there was even a moth eaten old lion that the trainer had to half hold up in order to stick his head into the lion's mouth. We were prepared to scoff at that but Peter Murray, our resident altar boy- philosopher, said, "A lion is a lion. And an old lion can still gum you to death." This common sense observation restored our respect for the lion tamer in particular, and the midway show in general. This midway show was the main feature of our trip to the circus. We all went inside and took our seats on the benches.

The show was okay, but we anxiously looked forward to the main event. It was "Wrasslin." Now this was twenty-five years before Gorgeous George and fifty years before the World Wrestling Federation. But "wrasslin" it was. Amidst gongs and boos and cheers, two large gentlemen climbed into the ring. One was clean cut and well mannered. He smiled and waved to the crowd of altar boys who accepted him as their champion on sight. The other gentleman wore black and had a hood with cut-out eye holes over the top part of his face. He had a three-day growth of beard and looked authentically evil. He had a name something like, "Marvin, The Masked Monstrosity." He sneered at us and made threatening gestures as though he would squash us like ants if he could. We hated him on sight.

The match began and it rapidly became clear that Marvin, The Masked Monstrosity, had another character defect. He fought dirty. He kicked, butted, bit, and gouged - and somehow the referee never saw any of it. We howled our criticism and one boy actually tried to grab the referee's shirt and point him toward the fight. Fortunately, one of the priests nailed him before he got too close to the action and trampled to death by the two huge gladiators. Finally, Marvin pointed across the tent, the referee looked away again, and Marvin hit the clean-cut guy with the little stool from the corner of the ring. We booed and hissed our displeasure as our hero went down like a load of bricks, and the referee held up Marvin's hand and declared him the winner. But it wasn't over yet.

Marvin came to center ring and held up his hands for silence. "I can beat any man in the house!" he cried. Some of us realized that with a house full of altar boys and priests he might well be able to deliver on that boast. "I will pay $50 to any man who can last ten minutes in the ring with me." We all looked around hoping someone, anyone, would challenge the Monstrous Marvin. Someone did. From the midst of the 8 to 12 year old altar boys there rose a giant of a man. He was at least as big as Marvin, freshly dressed and with a crew cut like ours. "I will fight you," he said. "I am a Catholic altar boy like my friends here, and you need to be taught a lesson in good manners." We all looked to Fr. Flynn for a clue on how to react. He just smiled and said, "Well, if he's an altar boy, he's big for his age." Taking this as an endorsement, we roared our support for this kindred spirit. Our friend smiled and acknowledged our cheers. He pointed toward Fr. Flynn and said, "Father, I *used* to be a Catholic altar boy. Now I'm a college student at Holy Cross College in Worcester." That explained everything. Fr. Flynn gave him an approving wave and the cheering went on for another few minutes.

Marvin, the Masked Monstrosity, waved the cheers away. "All right," he sneered, "it's me against the altar boy. We fight until one of us begs for mercy." Then surveying the crowd of us he continued, "and none of you will see it because your show is over! This special match costs another 25 cents apiece, so get out of my tent unless you can come up with the money!"

We let out a collective gasp, followed by a thoughtful silence, followed by several little boy voices pleading, "Can we stay?" "Please, Father!" "We've got to cheer on the altar boy!" - and so forth. The priests were trapped. There was no way out but to tap the contingency fund and come up with the extra 25 cents per head it took to keep us in the tent. Fifteen minutes later the deal had been done. We were all in place to watch the Holy Cross Kid take on Marvin, The Masked Monstrosity.

The fight did not start on an auspicious note. Marvin kicked The Kid in the stomach and The Kid went down like a sack of potatoes. The referee didn't see it. One of the boys tried to get the ref's attention by throwing a Cracker Jack carton at his head ("A prize in every box"). That didn't work either. To our great joy, the Kid got up and came back into the fight with a vengeance. For the next several minutes, the battle seesawed this way and that while we cheered ourselves hoarse. Then Marvin pulled his infamous look-over-there-dirty-trick with the referee, who fell for it again! Marvin came at The Kid with the stool he had used to crown the first guy. He swung it at the Kid's head with two hands, but The Kid ducked and the stool hit the ropes, bounced back, and seemed to graze Marvin's head and disorient him. Now it was The Kid's turn. He moved in and Marvin never knew what hit him. He gave Marvin a few quick jabs, an openhanded roundhouse right, then picked him up and body-slammed him on the mat. Finally, he jumped on the hapless Marvin, pinning him down.

The referee began the count but Marvin yelled, "I give up! I give up!" and the fight was over. "Big sissy!" we tormented him. Once again, Goodness, Truth, and an altar boy had triumphed over evil. It made our day and someone led a cheer for The Kid, and then a cheer for the priests who had given us such a fine day. By two o'clock we were back on the busses and headed home, reviewing the adventures of the day.

"You know," Peter Murray said, "that fight was fixed." We were horrified. "Where do you think that big guy came from? He wasn't no altar boy, and he looked more like my old man's age than a college boy. Yes, indeed. That fight was fixed." We argued and discussed this all the way home and even into the early evening hours.

That night I reviewed the day's adventures with Nana. She wanted to hear all about it. The animals, acrobats, clowns, all of it. As usual, she would amplify the story with some similar experiences from her own past. When I told her about the strong man, she told me how her father and his brothers used to compete of a summer's night in Lixnaw. The village men used to see how far they could throw the blacksmith's anvil. Her father won nearly all the time. I figured a blacksmith's anvil must weigh a hundred pounds or more, dead weight, and carrying it would have been quite an accomplishment, let along throwing it. "That was part of it too," she said with a smile. "They would have short races to see how far they could run while carrying it. It made all the mothers and wives nervous but as far as I remember, no one got hurt and they all had a good time with it too."

Then I told her about the fight. She loved that. "So there was that full grown man," she marveled, "sitting right there among the little boys. What a grand and glorious coincidence it was." Did she think the fight was just a show, I asked. She smiled, "Well, we'll never know, will we? But it's like a story we hear from the Seanachai or one we tell each other. There's some truth in every story. As long as no one gets hurt, and we enjoy the telling, and maybe even learn a little lesson, what difference does it make whether it's exactly true or not?" And with that, she segued into a little story of her own:

Nana, The Leprechaun, and The Magic Lamp

"There was a boy named Sean who lived in a nearby village and was known to everyone by his poverty and his good nature. He lived with his widowed mother, who was not well, and he did everything he could to provide for them both. He raised a bit of potatoes here, did some chores for the farmers there, and ran little errands for the merchants. Like many people at the time, he had not the luxury of one job. It was the many little jobs that kept him and his mother alive and warm.

One day he was down at the bogs digging out the peat that we all burned in our stoves and fireplaces for heat and cooking. The peat was like our coal; only it grew in these swamps where it had been for a thousand or more years. The men dug it out, let it dry, and then it made the grandest and warmest cooking fire you ever saw or felt. But the bogs were deep and dangerous places. They were like quicksand, ye see, and ye had to watch every step ye took or ye could disappear into the depths of them forever and ever, not to be seen again.

Once, the men found a body that looked like it had been there since time itself began. They had the priest come and say a prayer for the poor soul before they gave it a proper Christian reburial. Ye never knew about the bogs. My father used to say, 'There are many things besides turf to be found in a bog.'

Well, this day Sean was at the bogs, digging alone, when he heard what he thought was a little cry for help. He looked around, but there was no one there but himself. Back to work he went. Then the little voice came again: 'Help!' This time he looked around more carefully and there, toward the middle of the bog, was a little man half sunk into the mush. It was a leprechaun.

Sean wasted not a moment. He crawled as close to the little
man as he could and pushed out his shovel, inching the long handle
towards the leprechaun. 'Grab that,' he cried, and the little man did
as he said. Then Sean, strong boy that he was, pulled the shovel
towards himself up the banking, and the little man came along with it
to the safety of the dry land.

The leprechaun just sat there for a moment and looked at
Sean. 'And is it my purse you're after?' he asked at length. Sean
shook his head no. 'Sure if I caught you fair and square I'd be taking
your purse, and that's for sure. But what man could live with himself
taking a fee for saving another man's life?'

The leprechaun nodded his head in agreement. 'I agree with
your sentiments in that regard,' said he. 'Now take this,' he said,
producing a little turf-burning lamp from his tunic. 'It will burn
bright and warm ye forever- and more to the point, it will grant ye one
wish as long as ye don't insult it with your greed. Let me see if
tomorrow ye are as wise as ye seem today. Thank ye.' And with that,
he was gone.

Sean took the lamp home and told his mother the entire story.
'I do not like to see ye in danger,' she said, 'but saving a man's life is
an act pleasing to God Himself, so I thank Him for your safe return.
Put the lamp to burn in the window now while we think about what
our wish should be.'

And so the lamp went into their cottage front window and
burned day and night without their adding fuel for a long, long time.
The people all around asked about it and heard the story from Sean
and his mother. Often times, the people would suggest a grand wish
Sean might ask for. But Sean remembered the little man's warning
about greed and thanked them for their efforts, but did not decide on
the wish itself.

Then, a very greedy man who lived nearby heard the story and
decided the lamp should be his. He had a big house and a barn and
animals and crops in the field but he wanted more. He coveted that
lamp. And he hatched a plan to get it. He put on an old cloak and
hood and walked through the village crying 'New lamps for old!
New lamps for old! Come bring along your old lamp and get a new
one for your trouble.' And he came to Sean's cottage where his poor

sick mother rested alone. 'Give me that old lamp,' he said to the poor, sick old woman, 'and I will give ye this fine new one for it.' Well, the poor woman was confused. She had forgotten Sean's story. And the man said, 'Do it now and I'll give you a shilling besides.' And she took the new lamp, and the shilling, and she gave the wicked cheater Sean's old magic lamp.

When Sean came home that night, she told him the story. She was beside herself with the grief for what she had done. 'That's all right, Mother,' he said, patting her hand. 'The shame is not yours but the deceiver's who cheated ye. I think he will be dealt with in kind - but we shall see.' And with another pat on her hand and a smile, he put his mother at ease and went back to his work.

By this time, the wicked man was back in his house gazing at the magic lamp. 'Ye are mine,' he chuckled, 'and with ye will come more riches than I ever dreamt of. But one wish is not enough,' he continued, rubbing the lamp, 'so I wish…for all the wishes I want!' And he laughed again, pleased with his own cleverness. But he was just foolish as well as greedy. Ye can never outsmart the Little People. The lamp glowed low and red and a little voice began to sing these words:

'Ye could wish for your need,
But not for your greed.
Now my fire is freed,
For no warning you'd heed.'

And the lamp grew hot and hotter until the greedy man had to drop it and run from his house as the floor caught fire. Then it was the roof, and soon the whole house and barn were aflame. And there was no one to help him. The flames just grew and grew, and spread wider and hotter. He barely escaped the cottage with his life, and could do little more than stand by and watch the flames eat whatever they touched. Soon everything he owned was gone. All was taken from him by the lamp, and his own greed.

Sean soon heard this story from several of the local farmers to whom the man appealed for help or work. They gave the fellow a job sweeping out the stalls. Every man deserves enough to live, but sometimes not more than that. Sean knew the lamp must be his own, the one taken from his mother. He went out to the burnt house and

there in the ashes, was the lamp the little man had given him. It was
cool to his touch. He took it home and cleaned it. It looked as good
as it did the day the leprechaun gave it to him. He put it back in the
window where it burned by day and night and no one ever dared
touched it again."

"And did he ever make his wish?" I asked.

"They say he did," Nana said. "They say he wished that he
and his mother could live as well as their neighbors for the rest of
their lives. No more or less than that—living as good as the
neighbors. The lamp thought that was a fair request and granted it.
Sean and his mother lived long and happy lives. They left the lamp
burning magically in the window to welcome friends and strangers for
a visit, tea, or shelter from a storm."

"Nana, is that story true?" I asked.

Nana smiled. "As true as it needs to be," she said, sitting back
in the chair to twitch the dial on her old cathedral radio and find her
evening radio programs. "As true as it needs to be."

Oh yes, I promised to tell you a bit more about our host for the
circus trip, the Pastor of Sacred Heart, Father John Mary Flynn.

Fr. Flynn was a good man who did everything that was
expected of him as a pastor and priest—and he managed to live well
besides. He had the first food freezer in his rectory that any of us ever
saw, and it was always stuffed with roasts and hams when such
luxuries were almost impossible to come by. From time-to-time he
would share the makings of a Sunday dinner with some parish
member who was in need of such assistance and/or had performed
some service for Fr. Flynn that went above and beyond the call of
duty. My brother George would bring us home a roast from time to
time. A family living next door to the church got the opportunity to
help out a great deal, often on short notice. Fr. Flynn would even
occasionally send something to the nuns in the convent of St. John's
Grammar School, although like many pastors of his generation, he
didn't want to spoil the nuns by giving them too much. After all, they
had taken their vow of poverty, not to mention chastity and
obedience. The nuns, both Nana and my mother agreed, lived several
economic levels below the priests and usually ended up on the short

end of the stick. Mother was forever dropping off what she called "leftovers" at the convent, although they were good-sized dishes she had made just for that purpose.

Fr. Flynn loved fast automobiles, and bought a new car virtually every year. My mother staved off any tales of scandal by saying that his parents were wealthy and they bought him a new car each year for his missionary work in Westminster. That was a little village near Fitchburg where he went each Sunday to say a special Mass for the local folk in the town hall. My father smilingly agreed with that assessment, but added that he wished the family wouldn't buy Fr. John the new car each year just after he took up the Annual Day's Pay Collection for the parish. People might think there was a connection.

Fr. Flynn liked guns too. He and my father would often go target shooting in the woods with their Colt .22 target pistols. Sometimes I would tag along and set up the stack of cans they would plink at, or nail up one of the man-size targets that Dad had appropriated from his Army friends at Ft. Devens. They were both pretty good too, and occasionally let me try a few shots on my own. On certain Saturday afternoons, Dad and his shooting buddies were invited to visit the city dump after it was closed to the public and help reduce the surplus population of rats who lived there. I think Fr. John made one or two of those trips too.

Fr. Flynn kept his Colt on the top shelf of a closet in the rectory. Once, a group of altar boys was spending a Saturday morning cleaning out the rectory closets when John Brooks, not the cleverest boy of the bunch, found Fr. Flynn's pistol on the closet shelf. He showed it to the others. Everyone was impressed. "Do you think it's loaded?" one of the boys asked. "Let's see," said John. With that, he put his hand over the end of the barrel and pulled the trigger. The Colt was loaded. It did what Colt's are designed to do. John was taken quietly to the hospital for treatment. The matter was settled without fanfare. The altar boys no longer cleaned the rectory without adult supervision. There was no publicity.

Fr. Flynn was an authentic character. He did his job, set a good example in his personal demeanor, ran a tight ship, and liked to

live large. He was also a very outspoken man. Here is another
memory of Fr. John Mary Flynn:

1949: Father John Mary Flynn Spreads The Faith
The Sunday Mass In Westminster

Our parish priest was Father Flynn, whose patience would wear very
thin,
With those who moved like cows in herds, and spoke their minds in
floods of words.
At Sunday Mass, you seldom sat, for more than twenty minutes flat,
He did not think that slow was dutiful, nor "long" meant the same
thing as "beautiful."
The Rosary on Friday nights, was done before they lit the lights,
And if responses weren't in kind, you could get many prayers behind.
He moved so fast, some folks got dizzy, but Father Flynn said God
was busy,
So when he had a prayer to say, he got it done the fastest way.
Father Flynn drove like he spoke: a squeal of brakes, a puff of smoke,
While Mother said, "He's got his stole, and off to visit some poor
soul."
And Oh!—The thrill of God's own danger, with our liturgical Lone
Ranger,
When he would choose me, to my joy, to be his Sunday altar boy.
On Sunday, when our Mass was done, we'd set out on our weekly
run,
Up to a little country hall, where Father Flynn said Mass for all
The country folk, who had no priest, but spirits that would be
released,
So to the Mass site we ascended—and that is where the rushing
ended.
The members of that congregation loved…a…lengthy…celebration.
And Father Flynn got vertigo, because they moved and spoke so slow.
He'd have a prayer said nearly through, unfollowed by this country
crew,
They gave each word its proper run, and he was through when they
begun.

This was no twenty-minute service, and Father Flynn grew tense and nervous.

For none of them, it seemed, felt free, to use one word when there were three.

So Father Flynn would glare and glower, the steeple clock would strike the hour,

And they would kneel…and stand…and sit, and he would think, "Get on with it!"

Each Sunday Mass was much the same, but once there was a Red Sox game,

And Billy Murray, with a grin, gave his two seats to Father Flynn.

A lunch in Boston—then the Sox! The Murray's had a private box,

And all it took—no sin or crime—was getting out of Mass on time.

That Sunday we raced out the door; he put the pedal to the floor,

He drove so fast my eardrums popped, then once again, all rushing stopped.

Some fifteen folks, with wrap expression, announced their need for full confession.

And Father Flynn, depressed indeed, began to cater to their need.

The first man took a quarter hour, and though he looked both glum and dour,

Our goodly priest did what was right, but kept the end of line in sight.

The last old lady did him in; she begged forgiveness for her sin,

Which was, she loudly thumped and cried—the worst of all: The Sin of Pride.

And Father Flynn said, "That I doubt! What have you to be Proud about?"

With that, he strode to center stage, and let them have his pent-up rage:

"Confessions wear my patience thin, when made up of imagined sin.

Real Mortal Sins leave grievous stain, unlikely from the smallish brain.

So go elsewhere to wave your flag—I'll not waste time to hear you brag!"

He waved them clear a space to pass, and thus began the Holy Mass. What did the people learn?

They say his talk just curled their ears, and set the Faith back fifty
years,
But they had learned that low-yield sin, got little truck from Father
Flynn.
And me?
I learned that in Life's Lonely Dance, there's lack of sin and lack of
chance,
I'm wary about people who, conveniently confuse the two.
And what happened then?
Westminster folk a church acquired, and Father John has long retired,
He made his speech, he made his name, and yes—he even made the
game.
The incident is closed and done, and best of all: The Red Sox won!

#

And now, a word about my good friend and real-world
counselor, that altar boy/philosopher, the one and only Peter Murray.
Every neighborhood had a kid that knew more stuff, earlier,
than anybody else his age. Peter Murray filled that slot in our West
Fitchburg neighborhood. He had a large extended family of older
brothers and cousins, many of them young vets from World War II,
who "told him stuff." He hung around with the street corner guys, and
he read everything he could get his hands on—including the 1940's
editions of the scandal sheets (which were mostly True
Detective/True Confessions/True Romance kinds of magazines). He
was also a born storyteller who was willing to share his vast
knowledge of the world with others, and a good friend. I wrote this
memory of him that, strangely enough, is more factual than you might
think:

1951: Peter Murray
"The Foulest Words Ever Spoken"

It wasn't that we weren't supposed to play with Peter Murray,
It's just that folks thought Pete was growing up in such a hurry.
Sister Helen noticed it, and so did Father Rowe,

140

"There are some things," they gravely warned, "man wasn't meant to
know."
But Peter Murray knew such things and -Oh!—The tales he spun,
He was really "Hot Potatoes" back in 1951.
His older brother, Richard, had come back from World War II,
With a duffle bag of stories, and each one of them was true.
Like the time the Nazi's trailed him for a solid day and night,
And though they couldn't catch him, all his hair turned silver white.
And his mother's brother, Andrew, could keep numbers in his head.
He knew all the statistics, every player, and each spread.
He never had to write a note, it all was in his brain.
He made himself a fortune with some bookie down in Maine.
His father's father, Patrick, hadn't seen a sober day,
Since the Black and Tans found out that he had joined the I.R.A.
They chased him all round Ireland, until he reached the pier,
And jumped a ship as it pulled out, and ended up right here.
And Marilyn, his sister, spent her evenings deep in prayer,
For some guy she knew in Walpole who had earned himself the chair.
Peter told me how they used fresh blood, when restaurants made
gravy,
And how his cousin Michael was a boxer in the navy.
If he saw me with a hamburger, he stopped to tell me how,
In excruciating detail, that the butcher killed the cow.
He told me what the riggers found, when they pulled apart the wrecks,
And of course he knew the finer points of making out and sex.
He told me Tales of Honor, and then Sagas of Perdition,
(Did Sister Leo know about the Spanish Inquisition?)
Yes, Peter Murray knew the inner secrets of the world,
And he spread them all before me in the stories he'd unfold.
Yet of all the things I learned from him, the childish fancies broken,
I remember best of all, he knew the "foulest words yet spoken."
He told me all about it, on a balmy August day,
And as best I can recall it now, it happened just this way:
His Uncle Billy got picked up, in that store beside the mill,
Where they found him one dark evening with his fingers in the till.
The judge ascribed his problem to an excess of libation,
And put him in the navy for a four year paid vacation.

141

And so it was that Billy joined the nautical profession,
And came to learn the foulest of the foulest, foul expressions.
"It was," he said, "in Zanzibar, where this crazy Greek from Crete,
Cleaned out a waterfront saloon, just threw guys in the street."
Uncle Billy fought beside him, and the Greek bought him a drink,
And told him why he got so mad, he couldn't even think.
"There is no man alive, my friend, whose heart will not pump juices,
If someone says, 'Boost Easy!'—or just whispers, 'Igga Mooses.'"
"Their meaning is so foul," he said, "that nobody must use them,
And death by inches is too good for those who would abuse them.
There may be pardons for most sins, and reasonable excuses,
But no one gets forgiven for 'Boost Easy!'—'Igga Mooses.'"
So Uncle Bill left Zanzibar, with this within his heart,
And the secret of these curses made him live a life apart.
He built a cabin, down in Maine, and there, among the spruces,
He lived life with the knowledge of 'Boost Easy!'—'Igga Mooses.'
L'envoie
It's 52 years later, and what's out there, I have seen.
And never once met anyone who knew what those words mean.
The Murray's have all died or moved, and Peter's out of town,
But I let it be my business just to try and track him down.
I got his note last Monday, and I wanted to get drunk:
Peter Murray quit the world, became a Trappist monk.
"I was reading Virgil's Essays, from the early days of Rome,
And came across this sheepskin, found inside a catacomb."

"They had wrapped it tight in oil cloth, and then bound it up with
nooses,
Inside I found the meaning of 'Boost Easy!'—'Igga Mooses.'"
I left the world to spend my days in prayer and meditation.
I understand these words now, and their awful derivation,
So save yourself, give up the search, the secret has no uses!
And if you don't, my sorry friend: 'Boost Easy!'—'Igga Mooses.'

Impressions of Money: How Nana Went Blind

I told you that Nana Ware never had much money. The few dollars that she received from her children were quickly distributed among the younger family members—like me. "Money is like butter," she said, "it's better if ye spread it around." And spread it around she did. The priest who came on the First Friday to bring her Holy Communion always got a dollar or two. She had my mother send money to the missions and to the Catholic radio programs she listened to daily. She sent a few dollars to the extended family that still lived in Ireland. I even got a coin or two for candy for extra coffee milk during recess at St. John's Grammar School.

This story is about her attitudes towards money, and what I learned from my older brother Leo about how Nana went blind some fifty years before. It will all come together at the end.

You should know that my father, Leo F. McManus Sr., was active in local politics as well as local business. He was in the auto parts business. He went to work for Motor Tire of Fitchburg as a bookkeeper shortly after he graduated from Bentley College of Accounting in the mid 1920's. He said that he decided to stay in that business after he lived through the Crash of 1929 and the Great Depression. He learned that no matter how tough the times are, people will keep their cars running—and the auto parts business was about as depression proof as a business could be.

Uncle George, of course, believed that only the paper mills were truly depression proof. They too had run through all the bad years. As Uncle George told my father, "There will always be paper. Even when there is no business at all, you still have to send out cancellation notices. That means paper."

Dad's business and political interests kept him busy traveling around the city to meet with all sorts of folks and us children often got to accompany him on his rounds. He knew a lot of interesting people.

There was Nick the fireman at Central Fire Station off Main Street. Nick was a natural with kids and while he and my father talked business they would put me in a leather helmet and seat me at the steering wheel of a huge 1930's hook and ladder truck. I would swing the wheel and pretend I was driving. One night I managed to set off the siren and the howl and screech inside that cavernous station was nearly deafening in its intensity. Off duty and volunteer firemen in the area came skittering in to help out with the emergency and they were less than amused to find a flustered little boy behind the wheel and at the root of the problem. I was banned from the fire engine. Nick, however, took it all in stride. "We must be more careful, that's all," he said. He spread pads and cushions and old greatcoats around the base of the shiny brass fire pole that ran from the upstairs sleeping area down to the action deck. I spent the next several visits sliding down the pole over and over again.

Actually, when the memory of the siren incident faded a bit, he let me back behind the wheel of the big hook and ladder too. This time, he switched off the power to the siren.

John Palmer was another old friend of my father's. His claim to fame was a cellar full of Lionel electric trains. A bachelor living alone, the trains were his hobby, family, and his passion. I had never seen so many trains—before or since. He had layouts and tracks that ran all around his large cellar. There were mountains and valleys and tunnels. There were trees and grass and even little streams with running water. He could run up to six trains at a time. They were mostly steam engines and they chugged and smoked and whistled their way all around the track at high speed. I was convinced they would collide in one horrendous train wreck, but they never did. John Palmer always knew precisely what he was doing and though they may have missed by inches, I knew it was all part of a well-conceived and well-executed plan. "It's all about practice and planning," Mr.

Palmer used to say. "A little preparation can even make playing more fun."

Lt. Ernie Duddie of the Fitchburg Police Department was another good friend. Ernie was a firearms expert who not only trained the Fitchburg Police, but also was good enough to do special marksmanship training for J. Edgar Hoover's elite F.B.I. agents. Ernie owned every kind of gun there was, and knew them inside and out. He frequently put on shooting demonstrations for various clubs around the city and my father would take us along to watch. Dad said Ernie was sniper deadly with a rifle, but it was his performance with the six-gun that fascinated me. He wore them in holsters by his side and upon notice would draw and shoot like a cowboy gunslinger, and inevitably blow the center out of every bull they had set up before him. It was just like in the movies I used to see on Saturdays at the Lyric Theatre with the likes of Tim Holt and Gene Autry.

Once, Ernie and my father took me to a shooting performance at the Sportsman's Show at the Worcester Municipal Center. The show starred Roy Rogers. Old Roy came out on Trigger and announced that one of his helpers was going to throw plates in the air and he would endeavor to hit them all from horseback. True to his word, the helper started tossing up plates and Roy started blasting away at them—from the hip, over his shoulder, behind his back, and under Trigger's stomach. He never missed a plate. Roy's six guns were as deadly in person as they were in the movies.

On the way home in the car, I made two deadly mistakes. I said, "Ernie, is Roy Rogers better with a gun than you are?" The lesser mistake was calling him "Ernie", but he let that go in the face of my questioning his skill:

"No, he is not," Ernie said emphatically. "Remember when I showed you what buckshot could do? How one cartridge holds a thousand little pellets that spray all over when you fire them? Well, that's what Roy was firing: Buckshot cartridges. Why, all he had to do was point that six-gun in the general direction of those plates and he couldn't miss. If I set you up like those people did Roy, you could have shot almost as well as he did." I never felt quite the same about Roy Rogers again. Later, when Roy teamed up with Dale Evans and showed signs of a romantic interest, I dropped him entirely and went

back to old bachelor Gene Autry, where I belonged. Everybody knew
Gene Autry could beat up Roy Rogers in a fistfight. He actually did,
by the way, in the first and only movie they made together.

I wrote a story about an adventure with Lt. Ernie Duddie too.
I'll tell you that one at the end of this particular tale.

One day, my father took me to the home of L.L. Sawyer, one
of Fitchburg's wealthiest and important men. His family had owned
the Sawyer Mills for over a hundred years, and literally thousands of
Fitchburg families had ties to those mills. Mr. Sawyer lived in a huge
old stucco mansion on Prospect Street that he told me his family had
built for eighty-five hundred dollars in 1895. The house was loaded
with military memorabilia from his family's collection over the years.
I remember one Civil War cannon, which Mr. Sawyer told me, was
still fired every Fourth of July to celebrate our independence. Mr.
Sawyer was old now, and a little lonely. A little boy who was amazed
by everything and asked a hundred interested questions amused him.
We talked and talked, or maybe my father and he talked and I only
listened, but I got to share his stories in any case.

Mr. Sawyer talked once about his college days in the 1880's.
He went to Harvard College in Cambridge. "My father gave me
twenty-five dollars a week," he said, "and out of that I had to pay for
my laundry, incidentals, and cover whatever little social expense I
had. At the end of every week, I was pleased to tell my father that I
had money left over. He would say he was proud of me and tell me to
put the money in the bank while he gave me the next week's
allowance. In my entire four years at Harvard, I never asked him for
a cent beyond that." I am not sure I understood the implications of
that story, but my father seemed to be impressed with it, so I was too.

Now, whenever I got home from one of these trips, my first
duty was to report to Nana Ware and tell her about my great
adventure. She was always interested, amazed (or maybe amused).
She held my hand in her's as she oohed and aahed and clucked and
generally expressed great interest in, and support for, my story of the
day's happenings. She always made me feel that this particular story
was the best she had ever heard.

There was one exception: The story Mr. Sawyer told me about
his Harvard days and how he lived on that allowance from his father.

When I told her the part about the money, the twenty-five dollars, she smiled. Then she gently chuckled. Finally, she laughed out loud. I didn't understand.

"God bless ye, child," she said, "sure ye wouldn't know what twenty-five dollars was like in those days, would ye? It were a fortune! Your grandfather worked for the mills as a teamster and when they gave him the extra time, and paid him for it, he might come home with ten dollars in his packet. That were a good week! They were the two of us and the seven children and the food and the rent and all the household expenses. We paid for it all with ten dollars in a good week. Mr. Sawyer could have lived and taken his meals in a fine hotel for twenty-five dollars a week, and still had money left over to put into his bank. God bless him too," she laughed, "for he was a wealthy man—then and now." She squeezed my hand and laughed until the tears came to her sightless eyes, and I laughed right along with her.

I met Mr. Sawyer one more time—in 1960 when I was out of the army and working for Bernie Dolan, a prominent local manufacturer of ladies' sportswear. I've added that story to the end of this chapter as well.

When I was talking about putting this book together, my brother Leo told me a story about Nana that I had never heard before. It was about Nana when she started to lose her sight and her consideration of her family and their financial situation at that time. I guess I was too young to hear this story, but she told it to brother Leo, and he shared it with me.

Nana and Impressions of Money

Nana said, "When I was a grown woman, we moved into a nice little house down by the railway bridge in West Fitchburg. There was your grandfather, George, and our children Michael, George, Charlie, Tom, May, and your mother Kathryn. Tom was the athlete, the boxer, and they said he had a great career before him. They called him Fitchburg's own Great John L. O'Sullivan. He was that good. I did not approve of this prize fighting, and I told him so. He took my hand and said, 'Ma, it is what I do best.' He was the headstrong one, my Tom. My own mother said that a parent is sometimes closest to the child who causes them the most worry and heartbreak. I was that close to Tom.

He was coming home from one of his matches, walking along the Boston & Maine Railway tracks one night, when two trains approached from different directions. The one he saw drowned out the roar from the one coming from behind him. He leapt from one track onto the other—just in time to be hit by the second train. That's how I lost my first son. I think about him and pray for him to this day. Ye never forget the loss of a child, even if ye live to be as old as me. The memory stays that fresh.

In our home, we had a big old wood-burning stove in the kitchen, for cooking and heating, and a fireplace in the parlor. That's all the heat we had in the whole house, so in the wintertime they were going all the time. It took lots of woods to keep us warm and of course there was no money to buy it. Your grandfather and the boys cut their own.

On Saturdays, when there was no work in the mills, the lot of them would go off into the woods and chop down trees, cut and split them for the stove and fireplace. They had rigged up a sled to drag the wood home. Your grandfather would borrow a horse from the mill stable to pull the wood home. On a good long day, they could chop, split, and bring home some six or even eight cords of wood. He used to tell the boys they would be thrice heated from the wood: Once when they chopped it down, the second time when they split and stacked it, and the third time when it burned in the fireplace. That was one of his great stories.

We used most of the wood ourselves, but once in a while your grandfather would sell a cord or two to the neighbors. He could have got more for it, but he only took a dollar or two from them. 'We're all alike here,' he'd say, 'and no friend will go cold when we have wood to spare.' Sometimes, he even gave some wood away if the need was there and the money wasn't.

The girls and I used to split the wood further to make kindling for the stove. We would go out with the axe, stand a log on end on the chopping block, then whack into as small pieces as we could. Then, we'd take a hatchet, and chop it into smaller pieces yet so it would be just right to catch fire quickly and burn hot in the old kitchen stove.

One cold morning after your grandfather had gone to work, and the children gone off to school, I went out by myself to cut a little extra kindling to get us through a cold day. I stood the log on end as I always did and gave it a great swipe with the axe. And then I fell down with a great pain. I have never known such pain as I felt then. My eyes burnt and my head throbbed and I knew I was going to faint. I must have screamed, because all the women in the houses around us came running out to see what the problem was. They came out with their brooms and shovels and mops, for if there was a troublemaker in the neighborhood, he was going to meet his match in this little army of wives and mothers. They saw me on the ground and came running over to me. They carried me into my house and set me down on the little bench near the kitchen table. One of them, my friend Gert, looked me over closely and said, 'Mary, ye got a wood chip in your eye from the log. We will have to take it out.'

I crossed myself. 'Go ahead,' I said.

The women held me firmly, but gently, while Gert went into my eye with a sharp pin. She plucked out the piece of wood, but not before I fainted from the pain. When I woke up, I was on my own bed. My eye had been dressed and bandaged and they gave me something for the pain. There was no talk of doctors. There was no money for it, and no need for it. I trusted Gert to do as good a job as any doctor.

I was back at my chores the next day, and didn't think too much more about it. I prayed and waited for the eye to get better but, as the months wore on, I noticed that my seeing was not getting any better. In fact, it was getting worse. At first, I couldn't see far off but I could see up close to read and do my work. It wasn't that much of a bother except when the pain got bad. Gert made me a poultice. I used to put it on my eye and then I'd go lie down for a while and it would feel a bit better when I got up. Your grandfather would say, 'Go to the doctor, Mary. Your health is worth the bit it would cost us.' I didn't do it. In another little while I noticed I was not seeing that good up close either. It was hard to read, for example. One of my friends gave me an old pair of reading glasses she had, and for a

149

while they seemed to help. But I got headaches from them, and it started getting darker all around me, and I said to your grandfather, 'It's time to see the doctor.'

The doctor was downtown, a good walk away. One fine spring morning the two of us walked in to see him. He was a kind and gentle man, God rest his soul. He looked into my eyes for a long time. He took the glasses I had been wearing and studied those for a while too. 'Don't use these again, Mary,' he said. 'They will burn out your eyes like fire burns out a building.'

'How bad is it then?' I asked.

'Mary,' he said, 'it is very bad. Your eye was seriously damaged, and now the harm has spread to the other. I fear you are going blind.'

'Going blind.' I said it after him like I was hoping I had heard him wrong and he would correct me. 'And what is to be done?'

'I can give you something to help with the pain,' he said, 'but beyond that there is not much to be done here. We might slow down the process a bit, but we cannot reverse it. If we could get you to Boston, they have an operation there that might help. It could resolve the situation. It is certainly worth the try.'

'Operation?' I said. 'And how much would such an operation cost?'

'About one hundred dollars.'

Leo interrupted her story, "And did you do it, Nana?" he asked.

She laughed, "We had ten dollars a week then in a good week. One hundred dollars might as well have been all the money in the world."

"But what did Grandpa say when you told him?" Leo asked.

"I never told your grandfather about the operation," she said, "where was the sense? He was already working too hard and sick with worry about me. Why would I tell him and just make him feel worse yet? I told the doctor to keep that part about the operation between us two, and he agreed. He understood. We walked back home together, me leaning on his arm for strength. We didn't need much talking about it. We both knew how it would end. By the start of that same winter, I was as blind as I am now."

150

"And that was the story of the hundred dollar operation that Nana could not afford, and would not even mention so as not to hurt the man she loved," Leo said. "To this day I cannot spend a hundred dollars on an evening out without thinking how the lack of that hundred dollars put Nana into darkness for the last fifty years of her life."

I said I would tell the story of my adventure with my father's good friend, Police Lieutenant Ernie Duddie. Here it is:

1947: Police Lieutenant Ernie Duddie And The Old Majestic Movie Theatre

The Majestic was a showplace back in 1934,
And the finest names in Fitchburg would queue up at its front door.
Red carpets ran the lobby, through bronze doors, into the street,
The doormen were dressed up to look like admirals of the fleet.
The movies were the finest; you could feel the adulation,
For the likes of Douglas Fairbanks, or the film, "Birth of a Nation."
Houdini played this theatre, and they still spoke of the squeals,
From the children, as they trussed him up and hanged him by his heels.
But the glamour of the Thirties soon become a Forties slump,
And by 1947, the Majestic was a dump.
It wasn't that the management had let the place run down,
The Majestic's end of Main Street was the wrong side of the town.
And Vaudeville was all over now, so no one used the stage,
The furnishings all showed the wear and tear of use and age.
The owners kept it open, and they ran it day-to-day,
But in 1947—the Majestic passed away.
The whiff of popcorn yielded to the stench of stale cigar,
As they changed the Crystal Lobby to a low-end, seedy bar.
They took their rent from whence it came, so no one thought it strange,
When they rented out the basement as a Civic Pistol Range.
And this is where my story starts; my father's closest buddy,
Was Lieutenant of Police and Marksman First Class, Ernie Duddie.

When it came to pistol marksmanship, the Duddie aim was crack,
And every round he fired found its way into the black.
He put on shows around the state; he trained the F.B.I.,
And if Ernie had you in his sights, you'd best prepare to die.
On Sunday afternoons in the Majestic's shooting gallery,
Beneath the bar, down many stairs, he'd supplement his salary.
He'd do his tricks for G-Men and for clubs like Rod & Gun.
For member drives, and charity, and simply having fun.
My Dad and I would watch him; it was quite the Sunday lark,
Watching Ernie Duddie's gunplay in the damp and gloomy dark.
He'd put six rounds into the black and blow the bull away.
He'd fire six through one small hole, and make it look like play.
He'd draw and fire cowboy-style, and once they made him prove,
That he had really fired—because no one saw him move!
And then they'd pop new targets up, at different lows and highs.
They looked like bad guys, and went down with holes between their
eyes.
Through all of this, a small boy's favor smiled on Ernie Duddie.
In case I didn't tell you, he was father's closest buddy.
One Sunday Ernie brought in friends and one police recruit,
Who looked good in a uniform, but couldn't draw or shoot.
So Ernie taught him safety, "Aim it up, and down the range,"
He helped him get the feel of it to scare away the strange.
He showed him how to load and shoot—first standing and then
kneeling.
The gun went *Bang!* The guy went pale. He'd put one through the
ceiling.
He'd put a round right through the roof! He stood there shocked and
awed.
The echo died away and Ernie whispered, "Oh my God."
My father said it first. He said, "It isn't very far,
Through hardwood floors and cobwebs to that upstairs crowded bar."
The rookie was in shock, and down his face the sweat was streaming.
My father helped again. He said, "At least nobody's screaming."
Then Ernie was in charge again, "I'll go see what he did."
And then, just to my father, said, "I better take the kid."
Now, how a kid could make things right, I didn't understand,

But there wasn't much discussion time, when Ernie took my hand.
We walked upstairs into the bar; he swung me on a stool.
"The kid will have a Coke," he said, "and I'll have something cool."
No one ever questioned Ernie; they just did what he had said,
I sipped my Coke and turned to see the Wounded and the Dead.
I looked across the dance floor—and I saw the very spot!
The jukebox played so loud they hadn't even heard the shot.
Ernie saw where I was looking; he walked over to my chair,
He told me not to speak or point or (God Forbid!) to stare.
The bullet left a jagged hole, and then went through the ceiling.
While all around the dance floor rang the sound of laughter pealing.
Among those merry tunes, a single bullet made its way.
And no one ever knew how close that Death had come that day.
Then Ernie walked across the floor, as lightly as a cat.
He smiled and said hello to folks while patting splinters flat.
He came across and got me, and we left the smoky airs,
To walk across the lobby and rejoin the men downstairs.
And Ernie told them what we found, and said that all was well,
Then he took aside that rookie, and he really gave him hell.
"That's quite a day," my father said, "and if you want another,
You'll keep it to yourself and never—ever—tell your mother."
And so I haven't, until now, and you may find this strange,
But I never go out dancing but I think about that range.
I think of the Majestic, and the barroom, and what's more,
I think about the Forty-Five that ate the hardwood floor.
And I think about my father, and my father's closest buddy—
Lieutenant of Police, and Hero First Class, Ernie Duddie.

#

And one more tale. This time about old Mr. L.L. Sawyer, the old gentleman I visited with my father. Mr. Sawyer was the wealthy old gent who managed to get through Harvard on $25.00 a week spending money in the 1880's. I can still hear Nana chuckling when I write that line even today.

Some 15 years after that first adventure with Mr. Sawyer, I was a young man in my 20's working for Bernie Dolan. Bernie ran

Milady Fashions, a small garment firm manufacturing ladies sportswear. He operated from an old mill building that had once been owned by Mr. Sawyer. Bernie owned the building, but Mr. Sawyer had managed to insert a hook into the deal that made Bernie's life miserable. It happened this way:

1960: L.L. Sawyer Manufacturing Co., Inc.
Milady's Fashions, Inc.
Bernie Dolan, President
"Family Fashions at Fantastic Prices"

Louis L. Sawyer sold Bernie Dolan his business and building when he retired at the age of 65,
With the understanding that he could maintain an office there as long as he was alive.
That seemed a fair deal at the time,
But 30 years later, in 1959
Old Mr. Sawyer was still alive!

Meanwhile, Bernie's business had prospered and grown, and surrounded the little office without redress,
Until it resembled, as Bernie put it, "A pimple on the ass of Progress."

The old man hadn't used—or even visited the office in the 30 years since they had struck the deal.
But his stuff was there, and whenever Bernie brought it up, the old man would laugh and slap his leg and ask Bernie if he really thought he'd gotten such a steal.

Bernie, more than once, said he'd like to buy it,
And the old man would say, "Good idea! Go ahead and try it!"
Then he would quote Bernie a sum of money that was more,
Then Bernie had paid for the entire business and the building those 30 years before!

Bernie hated that office, and he hated the old man who had outfoxed him—but he was powerless to do much more.

So he'd rant and rave and kick the walls and stomp the floor.

In 1960, when I came to work for Bernie, old Mr. Sawyer was in frail health. He was dying, that much is true,
And Bernie would say, "He's at Death's Door—let's all hope the doctors can pull him through."
And finally, a year later, it happened without a bang or whimper or even a peep:
The old man quietly expired in his sleep.

I went looking for Bernie to tell him the news,
For now, per agreement, he was free to do with office and contents, as he would choose.
I could not find Bernie, but I did hear the rattle, rumble, and clank,
Of some piece of heavy machinery, that sounded very much like a tank.

I ran to the old man's office, and there—alert and keen,
Sat Bernie, at the controls of the biggest damn fork life I had ever seen.
Long speeches were not in Bernie's store,
"The old bastard is finally dead," he swore.

And with that, he raised the blades, and smashed right through the wall,
Like some great battering ram—while all around him there did fall,
The plaster, bookcase, desk, the flotsam and jetsam of the old man's business life,
Was forever cut and torn asunder, like butter by a sharp, warm knife.

Bernie personally destroyed that office, then proudly surveyed the damage, and bid the rubbish men to haul away,
All vestiges of L.L. Sawyer, who had haunted him from 1929 to this very day.

There were many things I learned from Bernie, for in him there were depths of knowledge and feelings both extraordinary and great.

The Nana In The Chair, And the tales she told
An anecdotal biography of Mary Dunne Ware (1860-1956)

Including his single-minded devotion to the concept of revenge—and his infinite capacity to hate.

156

Nana Comes To America

I wish now that I had asked Nana more questions about the history that was happening all around her as she was growing up in Ireland, and after she came to America. She was a young woman when Custer made his last stand, and was in her forties when the Wright Brothers flew at Kitty Hawk. I know that before she lost her sight, she read everything she could get her hands on. I am sure she was well aware of what was happening in the great world all around her. It would be fun to know what she thought of these historic events when they happened, and what people of the time and place had to say about them.

We know that for a while she lived in Boston and worked as a cook and maid for a retired army general. He was a dignified old man who had seen service in the Civil War and in the great Indian wars that followed. His was a time in the late 1860's and 1870's when the government tried to get the Indians, who had been largely ignored while the country was at war, back on the reservations and away from the hunting and grazing lands they had called their own for so many years. My father told me about a Lt. General Nelson Miles who retired and moved to West Fitchburg about that time. I wonder if he is the same man who employed Nana. If so, there were many stories that might have been told. I learned that Gen. Nelson Miles was indeed a man of important reputation. He made his mark during the Civil War, where he won the Congressional Medal of Honor for continued bravery under fire. Afterward he was chosen by the

President to pursue the likes of Geronimo, Cochise, and Sitting Bull. It was to General Miles that Chief Joseph of the Pinz Nez delivered his famous "I will fight no more forever" speech. He was the most decorated soldier on either side during the Civil War. They wanted him to run for the office of President of the United States—but he had enough of it all and just wanted to come home and live out his years in peace.

My father remembered that the general went riding every Sunday in his neat little carriage pulled by the old cavalry horse they gave him when he retired. The little boys would line up at attention and salute as the general rode by. Sometimes, he would stop the carriage and speak to them as a general addressing his troops. "Straighten out that line, boys," he might say, "and tuck in those shirt tails. Good! Now you look like soldiers and a fine unit you'd make too." The boys would giggle and beam as they rushed to obey the general's commands.

The only other story I remember about him was that his neat cottage in Waite's Corner had cannonballs arrayed on both sides of the sidewalk leading up to the front door. I believe they are still there.

For a house servant like Nana, these times were the "Upstairs/Downstairs" years in the mansions of old Boston. The servants spent their days in the basement, where the kitchen was located, and slept at night in the top story rooms that had been prepared in what today we would call the attic.

"It was mostly cold and damp in the basement," she said once. "The women who worked there most of their lives had what they called 'The Servant's Ailment.'" She held up her badly gnarled hands. "Ye call it arthritis today. There was a cure for it too, or at least a bit of help. The older women said if ye went out barefoot in the grass before the morning dew was dried away by the sun, the coolness would relieve the pain in your feet and legs. Ye could let the coolness of it ease your hands as well. I did it once or twice myself. I think the peace of a beautiful early morning before the topsy-turvy of the workday was as comforting to the body and soul as any dew-dampened grass ever was.

The servants slept on the top floor of those big old houses, and there were backstairs to get up and down without disturbing or being seen by the family. There was no heat up there, save what rose up from the house itself and the stoves in the kitchen and the fireplaces in the family and reception rooms. It was painfully cold in winter as it was stifling hot in summer. The workweek was six days long, and sometimes seven. The rich Catholic families would make sure the girls got off for Sunday morning Mass, and the afternoon duties were light since the Church frowned on servile work on the Lord's Day. Some Sunday afternoons we would put on our best clothes and take a walk through the park or along the city streets. We would be expected to bring the children of the house along with us, so it was a bit of work too, but we never minded. It was a great change and a good time. However, mid-afternoon there was a cold supper to be prepared and served, and our attention was called sharply back to our work. It was a good enough life. There were a good many girls fresh off the boat who looked at us living in those grand houses and envied us our success."

There was one exception to our never discussing the historical events of her time. Nana had followed the story of the Titanic very closely indeed. When the great ship struck the iceberg and sunk in 1912, I think all the Irish in America identified with the tragedy. This was partly because there were so many Irish immigrants aboard who lost their lives in the sinking, and also because they had all been through such a voyage themselves and knew the terror of a long journey by sea.

"The life boats, there were never enough of them," she marveled. "The shipping company owners acted like it was a surprise there were so few boats aboard the Titanic to save the many more passengers on board. We knew when we came over nearly thirty years before that those big ships did not have enough boats for everyone. When we were up on deck for the morning and evening air, the men counted them. We heard them talking among themselves and saying things like, 'God protect us from the storms, for if there's trouble they'll save the gentry up top and the rest of us in steerage will drown like rats.'

The stewards would lock us below deck at night and during storms. They said it was for our own protection, and we thought that maybe to some point it was. The men shook their heads and said no.

It was to keep us in our place and make sure we didn't cause any trouble if things went bad.

Girls, who were traveling alone like me, were the most skittish. I had never been out of my village, Lixnaw, before I went to Cork on my own and got the packet to Liverpool to join the big White Star ship heading for America. I didn't know a soul. Then, as now, the people with more money than decency would prey on the poor girls traveling alone. Some evenings after they had been drinking, the young men from the upper decks would come down in their fine clothes and offer the young girls traveling alone money to take off their clothes. One time they offered a beautiful young woman $50.00 to take off the top of her clothes for them. Sure, these were people who'd be hoping to find good jobs in service at $10.00 a month, plus the room and board. It is a dark and deadly sin to tempt the poor. There is a special place in hell for those who use their gifts to lead the poor astray. The girl ran away from them crying and in shame.

Because of that kind of behavior, the older family men would offer the young women protection for the journey. That meant ye became a part of their family. Ye stayed with the wife and the older daughters and helped out by caring for the younger children. In this way you could enjoy the security of a family when you had none of your own. The women would say we were all decent, respectable people and insisted we be treated that way whether we were 'Margaret O'Grady or the squire's lady.' The women pretty much ran things in steerage. The men kept each other company most of the way, and the families got together for all the meals and again in the evenings. Sometimes we had music and dance, and sometimes there were great stories told. It was a good way to cross, and some friendships began in the lower decks of those ships for the three or four week journey carried on in the new world for the rest of people's lives.

Our trip was fairly calm. We had a few bad storms and some of the people got sick with the swaying of the ship, but there were no serious problems. We arrived in Boston harbor just six short weeks after we left Liverpool. What a sight it was at the docks! At first I thought it was a riot. There were people of all shapes and sizes, horses and wagons, traps and coaches, cranes and nets, and every kind

of noise that could be made by man or beast or machine. There was
such a roar and scraping and screaming, and smoke and sparks, that
one of the men said, 'Glory be to God, it looks like they're moving
Hell!' Ye would think the people would be bumping into each other
and knocking themselves into the water by the pier. But there was an
order to it all, and ye did what ye were told, and stood where ye were
supposed to stand, and kept your mouth shut and just drank in
everything that was happening around ye. I remember the sound and
the movement and the crowds. I can feel the excitement still today as
I tell ye about it.

There were businesswomen there from Lowell and Lawrence
and the mill cities. They were waiting for us to get off the ship so
they could be offering the single girls coach rides to their city, lodging
in their rooming houses, and fine, clean work in their weaving mills.
Many of the girls who had no family or plans beyond getting to
America took them up on their offers. I heard later it was a hard life
indeed that they signed themselves into. They had the food and
lodging and a bit of money, but the work was hard and the hours long,
and there was no life for them but in the mills and the friendships they
formed with each other.

I had the job with my father's brother Timothy in Fitchburg,
so I knew what to expect. He came to meet me in a wagon and took
my trunk and me to the station where we got the stagecoach to his
home in Fitchburg. It was a two-day journey and we stayed at a little
coach house along the way that was safe and clean. He told me all
about his family and his life in the new world. Uncle Tim was a good
man of business and had a fine life in a neat little cottage with flowers
and grass and trees. He had a son, Young Tim, who had been born
with crooked legs and who could walk but little and even then with
great pain. Our arrangement was that Uncle Tim would advance me
the money to come over on the boat. Nearly thirty dollars it was
altogether, and I would help take care of Young Tim until the debt
was paid off. That took a bit over two years, but I lived in their house
and ate their food, and shared in their family, so it was not a bad life.

The Dunne's used to have Sunday afternoon tea parties just
like they had in the fine houses in Boston. They say the Irish women
brought the tea parties to America because they had seen and worked

at them back home. When they had the house of their own, one of
their first things they did was to set out linens and hold little tea
parties for their family and friends. All the new Irish in town were
welcome to come by and meet Tim and his family and all the
neighbors. Many of the newcomers made their first friends in
America through the Dunne's, and some even got jobs through the
Dunne's and all the people they knew. Those were still the days
when some mills had signs on their gates, 'NINA.' It meant 'No Irish
Need Apply'. But, we still had our friends and the decent folk among
the gentry would still give a man a job and a chance if he showed up
every day and did the work. It was hard work, but it was honest
work, and the men were glad to have it."

Years later, in the 1950's, there was a humorist named Sam
Levenson who used to appear regularly on the Ed Sullivan Show. He
would tell funny stories about his immigrant parents' adventures in
America. He was Jewish, not Irish, but most of the stories were
similar to the ones Nana told. They were based on common and
shared experiences about coming to America from Europe in the
1800's. Nana used to love to come into the living room with us and
sit, listening to him on the big 12 inch console RCA television set that
my father bought for $375.00 in 1949.

One night, Sam said, "My father came to America believing
the streets were paved with gold. He learned three important lessons:

1. The streets were not paved with gold.
2. The streets were not paved at all.
3. He had to pave them."

Nana laughed long and heartily at that one. "Sure, that's just
what it was like," she said.

"One Sunday," Nana continued with her story, "Uncle
Timothy brought over a young man who looked like he was just off
the boat. He looked a bit familiar but I could not place him. 'Mary,'
said Uncle Tim, 'I want ye to meet someone from your very own
village, Lixnaw. Did ye know the Wares? This is their son, George.'
He smiled and shook my hand. We talked for the rest of the afternoon
and he asked Uncle Tim's permission to call again the following
weekend. The young man, George Ware, came back many a weekend

after that as well. We married two years later and that was how I met your grandfather. It was at the Dunne's Sunday tea social."

Nana was involved in just about every aspect of our lives.

Sometime in the early 1940's, my father bought my mother a new, electric washing machine. It was an Easy Spin Dryer and it came complete with an electric, versus a hand, wringer to squeeze out the rinse water before you carried out the heavy wash basket and hung them on the clothes line to dry. This was an early household appliance of the mechanized age, but it still took several hours on a Monday to complete, wring damp dry, and hang out the several heavy wash loads produced by a family of seven people. The term "washday" was more than just another name for Monday. It was a measurement of how long it took to do the family wash and hang it outside to dry. Then when the wash was hung outside, you had to watch out for the rain. Not only would the half dried clothes get wet again but also the rain might bring soot from the big mill chimneys that dotted the city - and the wash would have to be done all over again.

My mother was not mechanically inclined. It took her some bit of time to get used to the new washer. In the meanwhile, under her philosophy that "…if a little bit is good, a whole lot is better." She dumped the better part of a box of Ivory Soap Flakes or Duz into the washing machine. We frequently had soapsuds alerts when the stuff frothed over the top of the machine and spread all over the cellar in great, white, sticky waves. I thought it was great fun. I used to run through it like Superman would run through a steel door. Leo and George, who had to clean it up, found it a lot less fun. The stuff left an oily finish on everything it touched and the wiring, plumbing, and even the furnace had to be wiped down before my father got home and saw yet one more washday mess.

The outcome of all this was that our clothes sometimes came out super-saturated with soap and were stiff as a board. No starch was ever needed in our family wash. Nana naturally did whatever she could to help solve the problem. She would rub the clothes worn next to our skin until they softened and became wearable. I can see her now, holding a pair of my socks that looked like dried fish and rubbing them together with her arthritic hands until they were soft and warm and comfortable once again. This was often an occasion for a story. One day, she told this story about my grandfather George, the mill owner's young daughter Blanche, and a beautiful pony named Top Hat.

Grampa Ware, Young Blanche, and Top Hat

"I told ye that your grandfather Ware was a fine horseman. No one had the touch that he did with those grand beasts. When he was the teamster on one of those great wagons, pulling the giant rolls of paper from the mills to the cutters, or just riding one of the company's saddle horses around the exercise yard, he was a master of his trade. The mill boss told him once that he would give a great deal to be able to ride like that, one with the horse, and the people watching him not knowing where the horse ended and the man began.

He took care of those horses like they were members of his family. It was like they could talk to each other and sometimes he'd say something only half aloud and one of the horses would come over to him and nuzzle him as if in response. Your grandfather was not an angry man, nor was he a man with a high temper, but he did go after a man once and they say he might have hurt him dearly were the other mill workers not there to pull him away.

It all started when one of the boss' nephews, a grown man who had not done much more on his own than take money from the family for fine schools and a house, and now a big job with the company, fancied himself a great horseman. He would come down to the stables and tell the grooms and handlers all about his great adventures on horseback and the like. Sure, these men had been handling horses all their lives and they knew right away that he was all talk and knew little about the subject. But—he was a boss' nephew, so they treated him with respect and no one ever told him what they really thought. He came to think of himself as one of the boys, but the men never trusted him. The story was around that in one of the other mills he had made friends and put the men at ease with his company. Then one day, he asked them where they went to have a smoke. In those days you lost your job for sneaking away for a smoke, but the men trusted him. They showed him where they went once in a while for a pipe. The next day when they went there, the mill boss was waiting for them. He fired the lot of them on the spot. They knew how the boss had found out.

At this time, the owner of all the mills had a beautiful young daughter named Blanche. She loved horses. For her 16th birthday, her father gave her a fine, beautiful, black pony of her own. It cost a great deal of money, and was the best horse in Fitchburg at that time. She called that horse Top Hat, and she loved him dearly. She brought him to the stables where your grandfather worked, and when she saw the hand he had with her Top Hat, and the way the horse trusted him, she would have no one else but your grandfather touch him. The word came down from the boss himself, no one but George Ware was to care for Top Hat. Sure, your grandfather loved that horse as much as she did, and he admired the bright and pretty young woman who was so kind, and had such good manners with the help, and who loved horses as much as he did.

One day, when your grandfather was away on a delivery with the team and wagon, the nephew, Bertram was his name, came down to the stable to see this fine horse that his uncle had given the young woman, Blanche. 'Saddle him up, boys,' he said, 'I'll take him for a ride around town and see what he is worth.'

The men told him that word had come down that no one but George Ware was supposed to touch the horse, let alone ride him. Sure, it was forbidden. 'Remember your place, boys,' he said. 'Now saddle him up as I said or the lot of you will lose your jobs this very day.' The men didn't like it, but he was a boss, so they did what he said, and away he rode on Top Hat.

When your grandfather came back, the men told him what had happened, and how Master Bertram had taken the horse for a gallop. Your grandfather was gone to the rage. The horse was his responsibility and that blackguard had no right to take Top Hat without the girl's permission. He went out to the paddock and paced back and forth worrying his pipe and praying for Top Hat's good health.

Some two hours later, Bertram came back with the horse. Have ye ever seen a lathered horse, boy? It happens when ye ride a horse too fast and too hard. They lather up like they were covered in soap and their breath comes in great gasps. Their heads are down and sometimes they limp. Unless they are wiped down and walked, they can cramp and die of the lather. The great heart just gives out and they fall down never to rise again. This is how your grandfather saw Top Hat, as Bertram urged him across the paddock towards him.

'Quite a runner, he is,' Bertram laughed, 'but not with the endurance I'd want to be racing him. Fine for the girl, perhaps, but not a real man's horse at all.' Bertram climbed down from the saddle and handed the reins to your grandfather. 'You'd better clean him up now, boy,' he said, 'we wouldn't want the pretty little cousin to know her precious Top Hat was off for a run with the grown-ups today.' Your grandfather grabbed the reins from the man's hand and said, 'Ye had no right to ride this horse without permission, and you deserve to be thrashed within an inch of your life for what ye did to him.'

'Well,' said Bertram, 'that pretty little speech just cost you your situation. Get out of here now. You don't work here or anywhere else in my uncle's company as of this moment.'

Just then, they heard a scream, and the girl Blanche came running across the yard toward them. Her father had brought her down to see Top Hat in his own carriage. When she saw the horse's condition and Bertram with the sneer on his face, she knew at once what had happened. She screamed and cried and took her riding crop to her cousin's face, and cut him badly. 'How dare ye,' she cried over and over again, 'How dare ye.' Bertram fell to his knees holding his face but she kept up the reign of blows to his neck and shoulders.

The men wouldn't interfere. They said they had no place touching a young woman of station, but of course they were all secretly cheering her on and watching Bertram take the beating he so richly deserved. Eventually, her father, the boss himself, came over and put his arms around her. 'There, there, my dear,' he said, 'don't upset yourself in this way. George will make Top Hat new again, won't ye, George?' Your grandfather said indeed he would and walked away with Top Hat to dry, rub him down and walk him until the seizure passed.

Well, the boss talked to all the men himself and soon found out what had happened. He was very upset at Bertram, the nephew. Bertram tried to have your grandfather put out for speaking to him so rudely, but the boss said he was lucky that your grandfather didn't give him the beating instead of a little girl. And quite the beating it was too. Your grandfather used to say that the little girl gave her cousin a fine switching. They say he carried the scars of it to remind him all the days of his life. His uncle forbade him from visiting the stables ever again. They finally ended up sending him to another part of the company a long way away for, though he wasn't much good, he was still family, and he would have a fine job for the rest of his life.

And Blanche rode her beautiful, black horse, and your grandfather cared for them both. Blanche grew into a fine young woman and married and raised a family of her own. Once in a while she would come back to the stables as a grown-up to see your grandfather, wish him well, and hear him tell his fine old stories about the glories of her wonderful horse, Top Hat.

The end. Did ye like that story?"

Nana & The Second Biggest Giant

West Fitchburg in general, and Temple Street in particular, were enclaves of civility during the 1940's. The women actually held the occasional tea party in our neighborhood. Not just sitting around a table, having coffee or tea and sharing gossip, but actual get-dressed-up-and-go-sit-out-in-the-garden-on-a-summer-afternoon tea parties. Miss Agnes Woods, the schoolteacher who lived in the old white farmhouse on the corner, and Aunt to Jerry Woods, one of my boyhood's best friends, would host the occasional garden party for her elderly mother who liked to stay in touch with the neighbors. Sometimes they were watermelon parties. There would be stacks of watermelon slices on china trays. Nearby were linen napkins and little silver knives and spoons. You ate all the watermelon you wanted. Miss Woods would collect the watermelon rinds at the end of the day and put them up as pickled preserves, much like the half sour pickles she made in the fall. Pickled watermelon rinds are another example of a cultivated taste.

The neighborhood mothers would scrub up their grubby little kids, like me, dress them in their Sunday clothes, and take them to Miss Woods' front yard garden, by the pollywog pool. Most often it was for tea, cookies, little cucumber sandwiches, and scintillating conversation. In retrospect, it was really well done and made a lasting impression.

West Fitchburg people tended to be friendly, peaceful, and generally minded their own business. Unless, of course, your business was more interesting than their business. Then they had no choice but to poke their nose in and find out what was happening. We had a woman in our neighborhood like that. She made a habit of watching our house. I suppose with the whole extended family in and out at all hours of the day and night it was just a lot more interesting than her own more solitary life. Whenever something went on that intrigued her, she would call my mother and press her for the details. Mother, being the salt of the earth type, would tell her the whole story. This annoyed my father. Many things annoyed my father, but nosy neighbors were on his top ten lists of annoyances. Therefore, he would torment the woman by doing mysterious things about which my mother knew nothing. One of his favorites was the empty carton trick. My mother was always after him to bring empty cartons home from work for storing seasonal clothes, or packing gift boxes for the cousins in Ireland. My brother Leo used to say that if you put something down in our house, and didn't touch it for a week, it was in a carton and off to Ireland and you would never see it again.

My father used to bring home these cartons in a dramatic way. He would park outside his big, old, cinderblock garage, and look around as though to be sure he was alone and unobserved—knowing, of course, that our neighbor was watching him all the time. Then he would take the cartons out of his car trunk, one at a time, and struggle into the garage with them as though they held a great weight. Between cartons he might stretch and rub his back. Then, off he would stagger with the next empty box, well knowing that our neighbor was practically falling out of her window with curiosity. That night at supper my mother might say, "Lena called today and asked what those heavy boxes were that you stacked in the garage."

"Oh," my father would say, "you mean your empty cartons?"

"Yes," mother would say, "that's what I told her but she got very sniffy and said that if she wasn't supposed to know, she would not ask again."

"Very strange," my father would say, hiding his smirk behind his newspaper.

As for West Fitchburg in general, everybody knew everybody else. So, for a kid growing up this meant the odds were high that your parents would find out what you were up to from the parish priests, the nuns in school, a cousin or aunt, or the women with whom your mother socialized, shopped, talked over the back fence, or played bridge with. It was like a friendly little police state and not a good place at all for would-be evildoers.

However, it was still a tough paper mill town and if you went out looking for trouble, you could find it. I remember hearing my father's police buddy, Ernie Duddie, tell him about a mutual acquaintance who had defied a court order to stay away from his ex wife and had gone there drunk one night and hit her once or twice. "A few of the boys picked him up last night," Ernie said, "slapped him around a bit so he got the idea, then took him to the depot. They put him on the first train out of town and told him if he showed up again he better learn how to crawl because they'd break his legs." My father nodded and said, "Crude, but effective."

However, try as a boy will, sometimes trouble just comes looking for you. St. John's Grammar School at Sacred Heart Parish kept grades one through eight and had its share of playground bullies. It was a slow day when there wasn't at least one scuffle, or maybe a full-blown fight, somewhere in the schoolyard.

There was one boy, I think his name was Charlie, who was a couple years ahead of us and liked to pick on the smaller boys. At least once a week he would walk through the area where we played, pick some boy at random, and say, "Hey kid, where do you wanna get hit?" The idea, of course, was to select your best-protected area, point it out to Charlie, and hope he'd have the decency to hit you there. Looking back on it, "Hey kid, where do you wanna get hit?" was the only thing I remember Charlie ever saying. For all I knew that was all he could say. He may have spoken Outer Mongolian the rest of the time with the one, single exception of, "Hey kid, where do you wanna get hit?"

One day, he picked on me and asked the big question. I was no match for him in a fight, but I felt I might be smarter. I mentioned the names of two eighth grade boys who were known to be the toughest kids in the school. They had kids like Charlie for lunch— and he knew it. "Brud and Porky are friends of mine," I lied, "and they said they'd fix anybody who picked on me." That was all it took. Charlie actually mumbled some new words like, "Cancha take a joke? I was only kiddin", and beat a hasty retreat, never to be seen again in our patch.

After school, at our 3:30PM review session, Nana and I were talking about this over strong tea and buttered Graham crackers. She had raised four boys herself at the start of the century and knew something about the world in which they lived and the bullies who hung around the edges. "Your Uncle Tom," she said, "he was the boxer and into the fancy as they called prize fighting at that time. When he was a boy, he was not as quick witted as Mike or Charlie, but he was fast with his hands and strong as an ox. If any of the bullyboys picked on him, he wouldn't say anything, for he didn't know what to say. To their regret, they would think his silence was weakness and keep it up until he turned on them and went at them like a little wildcat. There was nothing to be done then but let the anger run its course or pull him off his tormentor. More than one bullyboy went to his home that night a great deal the worse for wear. However, the word soon got around to leave Tom Ware alone—and it wasn't so bad after that. Bullies are often cowards who pick on the weak and if ye put up a fight, even if ye lose, they don't like it. They go elsewhere to find fish that are easier to fry. Now, ye really didn't lie to this boy on the schoolyard. Ye tricked him, and that's fair. A trick is better than a beating, as Fin McCool found out when he met Ian, the Scottish giant. Go fill my cup with more tea, lad, and I'll tell ye about the second strongest giant in Ireland.

Fin McCool & The Second Biggest Giant

"Fin McCool was the biggest and strongest giant in Ireland, and a well known sportsman and brawler. He had cleared out all the pubs in Lixnaw at one time or another and in most of the surrounding villages as well. When there was a fight brewing that involved Fin, the word would spread and people would come from all around to put down their money with the bookmakers and watch the fight. I never saw him fight myself, but my father said it was a thing of beauty and a joy forever to behold Fin McCool in a fight. He was big as a tree and his arms were like logs. There was no sport from anvil throwing to roughhouse football where he did not excel. He was a good

171

husband to his wife Oona too, and was soon to be a father himself. Oona had their neat little cottage ready for the great day and Fin himself had built a huge cradle for the baby that the neighbors say would have held one of Mr. Fuller's great horses.

Well, across the channel in Scotland there was another giant named Ian who had quite a reputation there for the brawling and deeds of strength too. It wasn't long before the men on both sides started promoting a fight between them. It took a bit of persuading as to who would go where, but soon enough his friends brought Ian, the Scottish giant, over to Ireland and proceeded to set up the fights. Fin hid down by the shore when Ian arrived to see the likes of this famous giant. And what he saw frightened him. Big as Fin was, Ian was bigger, and he boasted and swaggered like no giant Fin had ever seen before. When he got out of the boat he grabbed hold of the anchor, which two men normally set, and whirled it around and threw it the length of the rope it was tied to. He was a formidable man. Fin had hoped it was all the talk and that Ian was better at boasting than fighting—but it was not to be. The men arranged for Ian to fight most of the other giants in Ireland and one by one, sometimes two at a time, Ian gave them a drubbing they would not soon forget. 'Bring me Fin McCool!' he would shout, at the end of every brawl, and Fin knew that the time was near when the fight would have to be. He wanted no part of it and told his lovely Oona of his fears. 'And if I don't go meet him, he will only come here,' Fin moaned, 'and call me out before my neighbors and family. I know I can't beat him and I'll never see you or my child again. If I could be out of this mess, my brawling days would be behind me and I would be the husband and father you need me to be.'

'I'll take your word on that,' said Oona. 'You'll see your child and your grandchildren too. Now get on with your chores, stay close to the house, and leave everything else up to me.'

It was just a few days later that Oona heard that Ian, the Scottish giant, was on the way to their cottage to call out Fin for the great fight. 'Now here's what ye do,' she told Fin. 'Ye climb into that huge cradle ye built for the baby and pull these sheets around ye. Don't show your face and follow me lead.' And with that she tucked Fin into the baby's cradle and covered him with the blankets. She

172

scarce had finished that when a voice like thunder boomed outside her door. 'Fin McCool!' cried Ian, the Scottish giant, 'come out and meet your better.' Oona went to the door and greeted the giant. 'Good day, sir,' she said, 'and would ye be Ian, the Scottish giant?'

'I would, lady,' he said, tipping his hat respectfully, 'and ye must be the Missus Fin?'

'I am,' she said. 'I don't approve of the brawling, but Fin heard ye were in town and went down the road to meet ye. Ye must have passed on the high road or the low road.' The giant groaned, for it was a hot day and it had been a long walk. 'Ye are tired,' Oona said, 'Would ye come in for some tea and sweet cakes before ye head back to town?' The giant said, 'I would indeed, and I thank ye for your courtesy.' Then, with a 'God bless all here,' he was inside the cottage and sitting in Fin's great chair, which fit him quite well.

Well, he had the whole pot of tea down in a gulp, and a stack of cakes that would have choked a horse. But Oona was used to cooking for Fin, so she knew what to do and just kept the tea and the food coming. 'Imagine that Fin,' she chided, as she bustled about the little kitchen before the turf fire, 'going off and leaving me alone with that baby. And him I can't even pick up meself.'

'Oh,' said Ian, 'and where is Fin's baby then?'

'Why, right there in the cradle,' she said, pointing to Fin himself who now sat up and cooed with the sheets all around him so you couldn't see his face.

'Glory be to God!' cried the giant, dropping the sweet cake on the floor and looking at the figure in the cradle who he judged to be just a bit smaller than himself, 'that crayture is a baby!?

'I'll thank ye not to be insulting my child,' said Oona, pretending to be upset, 'he is a fine lad and so like his father. Have ye never seen Fin then?'

'I have not,' said the giant. 'I have heard great stories about him but I never saw him with me own eyes.'

'Well, the little gossoon there just fits in the crook of Fin's great arm. Ye'll see soon enough for yourself when he comes back here to find ye. While you're waiting, could you help me change the baby's nappies?'

The giant looked at the figure in the cradle, gulped, and took his hat. 'I thank you for your kindness, Missus, but I cannot spare the time. I have a wife and bairn of my own across the water in Scotland and it's back to them I'll be going this very day.'

'Fin will be sorry he missed ye,' Oona smiled graciously as the giant headed out the door and down the trail as fast as his big legs would carry him. 'Godspeed!' she called, to his departing shadow.

Well, the word spread that Ian, the Scottish giant, had seen Fin and backed away from the fight. The story added to Fin's legend. However, his wife kept him to his promise and at Oona's urging he told them all that his fighting days were over and it's home he would be from now on, tending his little farm with Oona and her babes.

And that is how Oona and Fin McCool tricked Ian, the Scottish giant, and bested him without exchanging a single blow.

The battle," she said, signaling me for another cup of the strong tea and just a few more buttered Graham crackers, "often goes to the smart one and not the strong one. And a good woman who loves ye can get ye out of more messes than ye can shake a stick at."

Nana, Mary, and Cromwell's Haircut

I never had a chance to know my father's side of the family. This was because the McManus' were a small family to begin with (compared to the Ware gang, for example), and most of them died young (compared to the Ware gang, for example, who lived on into their eighties and nineties). The Wares and our cousins, the Beauvais, were all around me as I grew up in the 1940's. They lived in Fitchburg, Clinton, and Concord but we visited back and forth regularly and it was a rare Sunday afternoon that they weren't visiting us or we might be visiting them. We were close, and involved in each other's lives in a regular and continuing way.

Another reason I remember the Wares, is that they told better stories. Nana was, of course, the family master but other members of the clan had their stories too, and they'd tell them at the drop of a hat. They were good stories, often funny, and they had a beginning, middle, and an end. They often had a message too, but they didn't club you with it. They sort of led you to the stream but whether or not you drank was entirely up to you.

The stories that came down on the McManus side were light on fantasy and humor and heavy on duty and responsibility. They were stories to make you think, know your place, and behave. Like many of the stories the nuns at St. John's told us, they could be grim indeed. I remember once telling Nana Ware a story that a nun told us in class about a little boy who raised his hand to hit his mother. Could anything be lower than that—a boy attempting to hit his mother? Anyway, he was promptly struck dead by a bolt of lightning from a clear summer sky and fell down, crisper than bacon, with his hand still raised in the maternal attack position. It gets better.

When the priest finally decided it was okay to give the boy a Catholic burial and they deposited him in the family plot, his hand came back up through the ground. The hand that was raised against his mother would not stay buried. It rose above the earth to disgrace him even in death. They finally had to plant a bush over it so as not to offend local sympathies any further. This story came from the nun, and "Sister said" had the highest credibility of any story opener I ever knew.

I remember seriously telling Nana Ware this story. She listened patiently, as she always did to another's story, but try as she would, she couldn't hide the little smirk that appeared around the corners of her mouth. "Glory be to God," she said, "that's a powerful story, boy. Raising your hand against your mother is a serious sin, but I never heard of God, or his Blessed Mother, taking it this seriously before now. I wonder why they didn't bury the poor child a bit deeper. That would have solved the arm problem, wouldn't it? And did they bury him standing up that his arm would rise up just that way? Yes," she concluded with a chuckle, "that's a powerful story and deserves a bit of thought."

I thought about what Nana said that night in bed. It probably could not have happened just the way I told it—but I was sure I had it right. Maybe, I thought, the good sister was trying to make a point and chose to do it with a story that was more dramatic than factual. I mean, didn't even Jesus teach lessons through the telling of stories? They were called parables—but they were entertaining stories that got people to listen while an important point was being made. I understood what Nana meant: We should listen to all the stories we hear as we go through life—but it is up to us which of them we believe as revealed Truth, and which we enjoy and admire as a good example of the story practitioner's art.

However, many of the McManus stories were good ones too. I liked the story of The Gold Lady, for example. And I never tired of hearing about the Civil War general that fought Indians all over the old west—and then moved near my family to quietly retire. It's just that they had no chance against Nana—she told stories all the time. She would win out in volume alone, as she would be reminded of a new one by something someone said, or something she heard on the radio, or even a verse from a hymn or prayer might bring forth a new story, or at least a variation on an older one.

Another difference between the Wares and the McManus' was in the ways they looked at the grimmer realities of the world—like illness and death. To my father, they were horrific events to be mourned and contemplated over long periods of time. To Nana, they were merely continuations of a natural process that was all a part of some great plan she believed in, though she might not fully understand. I remember once when an elderly relative died after a long illness. My father's reaction was to legislate that we couldn't go to the movies that week, nor listen to our radio programs. It was in this manner that we showed respect. I remember my mother slipped once and said what he'd really like to do is drape the old Baldwin piano in the living room in black crepe like they did in the early 1900's, then sit around in the dark lamenting. She drew the line at that.

Nana's reaction was different. "Oh," she said, "it's God's will. We all have to go the same road some day. The poor soul is at peace now and free of the terrible pain that afflicted him for so long. We will remember him in our prayers." With that, she'd go back to her life with an easy heart. That night, she might forget and leave her radio on after her evening devotionals. One of my radio programs, The Lone Ranger, might be on. If I stood by the door, I couldn't help but hear it. Well, where was the sin of that?

Another interesting contrast between the two families was that my father had things that were "too good to use." I remember a gold pen he got one Christmas. It was a fine, expensive writing instrument, and he pronounced it "too good to use." It went into his top bureau drawer along with other such little treasures that didn't see the light of day until years later, after he died.

Nana, on the other hand, used whatever she was given. She thought the best thank you for a gift was for the donor to see it in regular use. I remember when the priest came to deliver her Holy Communion on the nine First Friday's. Nana would be turned out in her best dress, with whatever little piece of jewelry she had on prominent display. My mother would bring out two crystal glasses from some long ago family dinner service, and in these would be the drink that would break her fast. The brass crucifix and candlesticks that held the fine beeswax candles would be polished and set neatly on a little table in the living room, covered with a starched white linen cover. "How do ye think I look?" she'd say to whoever was nearby. "Like the old queen herself, no doubt?" And then she'd laugh her gentle laugh.

She always had a couple dollars in her pocket, and she'd give these to whoever needed them or, in this case, to the priest who brought her the sacraments. "That's all your money, Nana," I'd say. She'd wag her arthritic old finger at me and say, "Remember, my boy: Spend it and it's gone forever. Give it away and it comes back to ye and more."

Nana Ware was one of the three strong women who lived in the white house on Temple Street. Nana had raised a family of four boys and two girls, alone—widowed and blind. There were no agencies to help in those days; you did it on your own with the help of your family and occasionally, your friends. I never heard Nana complain about the unfairness of it all, or the backbreaking hard work that such a life entailed. A whiney "Why me?" was just not in her vocabulary. You did your job and moved on.

My mother, Nana's younger daughter Kathryn, was in her mother's mold. She cared for five children, plus her husband and mother, and once again did her job without complaint or ceremony. "I can do it," she'd say of whatever work came her way. "Kate's a good old horse."

Mother was a woman of her times in that my father was head of the family, keeper of the purse strings, and final authority on pretty much everything we did. Mother, however, maintained her dignity and got things done in her own way and on her own schedule. It was a rare time when things didn't come out the way mother had intended from the start.

Finally, there was my sister, Mary. Mary was the oldest of the five children, the only girl, and unquestionably the boss of our generation. She was also my sitter and friend. She often seemed better able to put up with a little brother following her around and disrupting her schedule and social life better than did the older brothers. I was often a member for the early evening part of Mary's social set—and she involved me in her activities. If her friends were coming over to study, for example, or pull taffy, or to make their God-awful vinegar candy, I had a role to play. It might be helping prepare snacks, or serving guests, or whatever. What mattered was that I felt a part of the scene and bloomed with all the attention.

Once, in the early Forties, Mary was invited to a Holy Saturday reception at her friends, the Fisher twins' house. Lent officially ended at noon on Easter Saturday so that afternoon, and early evening, were acceptable times to resume our regular living styles and schedules—and the Fisher's were having a quiet house party to celebrate the event. It was naturally a dress-up party, and everyone was attending in the new Easter outfits they would be wearing the next day. That included me. The Fisher's had invited me to the early part of the evening and my father agreed to pick me up and bring me home after an hour or two so the older kids could have some fun on their own. I had a new Easter outfit to wear, but everyone had forgotten to take me for a haircut. Mary delicately informed me, "You look like a dry mop." She decided to solve the problem.

Late that afternoon, when everyone was off during chores and getting ready for the big Easter celebration next day, Mary led me into our kitchen. "I will cut your hair myself," she told me. "I have seen it done hundreds of times at the barber shop and there is nothing to it." Who was I to argue?

She sat me in one of the painted wooden kitchen chairs, and upended one of my mother's larger mixing bowls on top of my head. "I will just cut around the bottom of the bowl," she said, "and that will give you a neat little trim. You will look quite handsome with your new haircut and Easter outfit." She began to cut.

I think she soon realized that cutting hair was tougher than it looked. First of all, I moved too much. Secondly, the bowl would slip down first on one side, then the other. The result was too much off here and not enough there. She would try to fix that and soon, it was too much off everywhere. "You look fine," she said, trying to

179

soften the horror I saw in her eyes, "Put on your cap and let's go quickly now."

We were dressed and out of the house in something under five minutes. We were at the Fisher's shortly after that. Mary's friends tried not to stare at my head as I removed my cap. Mary said, "I cut his hair." "Yes," said one of the Fisher twins, "we can see that." People smiled and tried not to look my way for the rest of my visit.

"Dad's here to get me," I said, looking out the window as his 1941 Chevrolet Deluxe (Massachusetts Registration 31483) pulled into the Fisher's driveway. "I better go now."

"It's cold," Mary said, pulling on my cap, which slid down over my head until it was stopped by my ears. "Leave your cap on in the car and don't say anything about your head to Dad until you get home." I did as I was told. It was a quiet ride home.

When we got back home, Dad's friend and our pastor, Fr. Flynn, was there, waiting for Dad to visit and spend an hour or two playing cribbage. He was a plain spoken man, and the first to notice my haircut after I took off my hat. "My God, Leo," he said to my father, "what happened to the kid's hair? He looks like one of Cromwell's Round Heads."

Now, I didn't know what that was, but it didn't sound good. I started to cry. My father who had finally noticed my haircut, however, soon overtook my theatrics. He went off on a rant of his own. "Who did that to you? No, don't tell me. Your mother has too much judgment. Leo and George wouldn't dare. It has to be Mary. Mary did it, didn't she?" I nodded yes through the tears. "Great! Easter Sunday and I got to go to church with a kid who looks like… one of Cromwell's Round Heads. I won't have it!"

By this time, my mother had appeared on the scene, and started assuring my father that the whole thing was a misunderstanding and/or completely under control. She whisked me out of the room so he couldn't get any madder just by looking at me and gave Fr. Flynn a sign that he should calm Dad down. She waltzed me into Nana's room and told me to stay there with Nana—while she called the Fisher's house and told Mary not to hurry home—at least until further notice. She knew Mary could do no wrong in my father's eye and it was just a question of getting him over his current reaction. After a few hours, everything would be fine again.

Well, not everything. I still had the haircut to deal with—and I told Nana the whole story. She clucked and coughed and smiled, now and again, but mostly took it as the serious matter I thought it was. "And on top of everything else," I said, "Father Flynn thinks I look like one of Cromwell's Round Heads."

"Cromwell," she spat. "Surely ye don't mean Oliver Cromwell, the Lord Protector of England and the Scourge of Ireland, do ye? A hateful man he was who believed that he knew what was right for everybody else, no matter what they thought or believed. He and his followers cut their hair in a round bob so they could recognize each other and called themselves 'Roundheads.' They overthrew the King of England and put Cromwell himself in command of it all. He forced his will upon the people and caused great harm and hardship upon the land. After a long while, the people tired of his ways and rose up against him. He was overthrown and died a bitter and broken man. The lesson of Cromwell is that evil people may win a victory here and there, but they never come out ahead in the longer run. The good will eventually win just as surely as the tortoise beat the hare. Cromwell, indeed! The less said about him, the better! When I was a girl the worst thing ye could say to your worst enemy was 'The curse of Cromwell be with ye!' And then ye had to go to the priest to be forgiven for the evil thing ye said. Cromwell, let him be subject to God's own justice! Ye don't look a bit like him," she said emphatically, patting my patchwork quilt of a haircut. I would have felt better about her assurances of my good appearance if she hadn't been blind.

"A mean and cruel man Cromwell was," she went on, "And when he came to Ireland he quartered his horses in our churches and let them drink from the Holy Water fonts as they would. He said of our barren countryside that there wasn't enough water to drown a man or enough wood to make a gibbet to hang him, or enough earth to bury him. The Lord and St. Patrick must have heard that. Years after Cromwell died the people still hated him enough to dig him up and then hang him—just for the justice of it. Aye, ye know they hate ye when they do that."

181

I decided to steer the conversation away from Irish history and more toward my own problem. "Do you think Mary will get in trouble for cutting my hair when she comes home?" I asked.

"Not a bit of it," Nana chuckled. "Pretty young daughters can charm their fathers out of a mood with a smile or a tear—and sometimes both. You can't be looking at a child you love and having angry thoughts at the same time. Girls have as much a gift of the blarney as do the boys—only they don't show it off until they have to."

"Blarney, that's the gift of gab. Everybody says that Dad's lawyer friend, Mr. Gurney, has the gift of Blarney"

"Indeed it is the gift of gab. The gift of good conversation and being able to come up with the right answers at the right time. Your father's friend, Mr. Gurney, is a lawyer. The gift of gab is a special gift from St. Patrick to an Irish lawyer. Shall I tell ye where Blarney came from?"

I settled back in the old rocker next to her chair and she began this way:

The One-Hundred and Twentieth Stair Of Blarney Castle

"They say that Squire McCarthy, the Master of Ireland's Blarney Castle never did what the English Queen told him to do. But - he said no in such a lovely way, so beautifully and respectfully, that the Queen could not bring herself to do him harm. 'Yes, Your Majesty,' he might say. 'Sure, your worldly beauty is matched only by your royal wisdom and divine goodness.' If anyone else dared try such nonsense in her presence she would cry, 'No more of your blarney!' and they best be about doing whatever she told them to do or the royal headsman would be after making a call on them. There are some things that one person might say that makes everyone smile and laugh, but if another says the very same thing there could be a great row.

But the Master of Blarney Castle had the golden tongue, and he learned the secret of it from his daughter Lilly, and she got it herself from the Little People. It happened this way:

Lillian was the princess of Blarney Castle. Lillian was her baptized name, but everyone in the family called her Lilly. She was a smart and a beautiful young girl, and though she lived in the great Blarney Castle she put on no airs for the villagers and they loved her dearly for it. They'd see her on the warm days out running around the castle grounds, playing games with the children of the village her own age, laughing and running with them in the gold summer sun made all the more yellow by her own golden hair. Aye, a treasure she was for all was Lilly belle, as they called her—but the child had a problem too. She would not speak a word.

Sometimes she'd form a word with her lips and people would wait for the sound to come forth—but it never came. She was all about silence. She was a bright and beautiful child who would not speak a word.

Her father and mother took her to the finest doctors at home and abroad, and to the clergy too, but it was all to no avail. Princess Lilly smiled and laughed in her beautiful way, but said never a word.

Some said it was a curse, some cruel joke of the Little People perhaps. They lived and worked and played in the woods all around Castle Blarney. Some said they were responsible for Lilly's situation. That's for sure, some said.

Well, ye have no right to blame anyone, human or fairies, when there is no proof. And this story came to the ken of the Little People and they did not like it at all. They had done nothing wrong to anyone worse than hiding a rake or a hat and watching the owner search for it while they hid in the brush and laughed. The business about Lilly, however, was serious. They loved the child too and worried about her problem. They would never harm anyone, let alone the beautiful Lilly, and they would have their honor restored.

The Little People talked about it among themselves. Their leader, the gentle and wise Lord Kevin of the Glenn, conferred with the older members. What should they do, he asked. The talking went on all one night and a day. It was the Good Jonathan himself who finally suggested that they send one of their own, the Queen Julia, to watch the child Lilly and discover, if she could, the secret of the silence. The Queen agreed and made herself unseen. She watched Princess Lilly day and night for a long time—but to no avail. 'I find nothing wrong,' Queen Julia told the others of her kind. 'She chooses not to talk, perhaps until there is something in her life serious enough to be talked about. There is nothing to be done now' And with that— the Queen Julia went back to her life of protecting the sacred and enchanted stone of Blarney Castle.

Do ye know about the sacred stone of Blarney Castle?

It seems long before the Castle was built, thousands of years before, the old ones who now live under the ground, had a magic stone. It was a stone of great power. Surely the most magical stone in that part of Ireland. It could grant a wish to any person of pure heart that touched it and made their wish known. But no one knew about it now except the Little People, and they said nothing at all about it. Their job was to watch over and protect their enchanted stone.

The stone was out where people could see it—although no one but the Little People knew that. Rather than hide their enchanted stone, they left it out where the builders would find it and use it in the construction of the castle. And use it the builders did. 'Such a fine stone as this should be a part of the walkway,' they said. And so, the enchanted stone became the one-hundred-and-twentieth step up the castle walk. Those countless people who had walked over it for hundreds of years had never known of its power. Isn't that the way of it? Sometimes the most wonderful things are right in front of us, and we don't know they're there. All those people who walked over it each day never knew enough to make a wish and claim the stone's power to make it come true. And that was the way the Little People wanted it. For magic attracts attention and the Little People wanted to live in as much peace and quiet as they could do.

Well, the years went on and on, as the years will, and Princess Lilly grew and was a young woman now. It was near time for her to marry. Her father had brought in gentle young men from families like her's all around the countryside—but Lilly had no interest in them. Kind and polite she was to them, and she smiled kindly and laughed gently, but much to her father's disappointment she gave none of them a second look. Her heart belonged to the village blacksmith, Sean, who she had played with as a child in the village. Sean was her best friend and she would have no other for a husband. Sean knew all this without her ever saying a word. At her quiet urging he went to see her father to make his case for Lilly's hand in marriage.

Her father near fainted at the proposal. Here he had imagined a life of wealth and position for his daughter in some fine family and she would be a blacksmith's wife. 'No,' he told them, 'it cannot be. The boy brings nothing to the marriage. Poor boys may never love rich girls. You must never see him again.' And with that—Sean, the young blacksmith, was put out of the Castle and told never to return again.

That night was a bad night for Princess Lilly. She lay awake in her bed, crying into the darkness, for the boy she might never see again. All this was seen by the Little People who rushed to tell the Queen Julia of this new occasion.

'I think it is time,' said the Queen, 'for me to show myself and make the problem go away once and for all.' The others agreed. With that, she was gone to the Castle on the wings of the wind.

Queen Julia found Princess Lilly weeping in her bed just as the Little People had told her. 'Enough crying now, my child,' the Queen said, casting off her invisible cloak and appearing in all her beauty and splendor. 'No problem was ever solved by a broken heart. Ye must do something if ye wish to sway your father and reclaim your love.'

Lilly looked at her with wide eyes and shrugged her shoulders saying, in her way, what is there to do?

'Ye must speak your heart, child. Ye must tell your father why this boy Sean must be your husband.' Lilly began to cry again, more helplessly now than even before. How can that be done, she asked with her sad eyes.

'There is a way,' said the Queen. 'It's the secret my people have kept lo these many years—but—I will tell ye the story for ye are a girl of good heart.'

Lilly stopping her sobbing and looked at the fairy Queen hopefully.

'There is an enchanted stone here in the Castle,' she told Lilly. 'It works only for the pure of heart and it grants them a wish if the wish is unselfish and brings happiness to others as well as to themselves. Ye must not pray small, just for yourself. Ye must pray large and include others if ye want the stone to hear. Go to the Castle walk. Count out and find the one-hundred-and-twentieth stone. It is the enchanted one. Make your wish and may the enchanted stone hear you and grant you happiness.' And with that, she was gone.

The next morning Princess Lilly was up with the sun and heading along the walk counting the stones to herself. 'Ten...fifty... one hundred...one hundred-and-twenty.' And there it was, looking much like the other stones around it yet now having a golden glow about it too. Lilly knelt beside the stone and silently made her wish. 'Please grant me a way to marry Sean the blacksmith, and keep me father's love and trust at the same time. Make all of us and the village happy in this way.' And when she was through, she bent down and kissed the stone.

Lilly felt something stir within her. 'And what am I doing just standing here for, then?' she asked aloud. 'Why...I can speak! I can say what's on my mind and in my heart!' And with that—she was gone to find her father.

Her father was sitting in one of his rooms sitting his tea and Lilly burst in. 'Father,' she said, 'we must talk and the time for it is now.'

'Lilly, child, ye can speak!' her father cried.

'Indeed I can,' she said, 'and it is time ye hear me out. Ye say Sean would bring nothing to a marriage and that is not so. He would bring his love, and his goodness and his faithfulness. And what more can one man bring than that? He would make me want the gift of speech so badly I would take advice from the Little People to make it happen. And now, my father whom I love, I would use that gift of speech to convince ye to grant me my happiness.'

Well, there was little more to be said. Her father's eyes grew moist as he embraced his beloved daughter Lilly and granted her this wish. 'Ye are the most eloquent child in Ireland,' he told her with a great hug and kiss.

And so, the wedding between Lilly and Sean came to be—and it was quite the grandest affair ever seen in those parts. Queen Julia, Lord Kevin of the Glenn, the Good Jonathan, and all the Little People attended in their finery and pledged their protection of the young couple and all who lived in or visited the Castle. Lilly had told her father the secret of the enchanted stone of Blarney Castle—and he kissed it too and became the most eloquent lord in the country. And to this day, people go there to kiss that same enchanted stone and earn themselves the gift of the Blarney.

And that is the story of the eloquent young woman who convinced her father to grant her greatest wish. And they all lived happily ever after.

The end. Did ye like that story?

The story of the Master of Blarney Castle and his beautiful young daughter would not be complete without my telling the story that partly inspired it. It is the story of our family friend, the honest and eloquent West Fitchburg lawyer, who truly had the gift of the Blarney, John Costello Gurney:

John Costello Gurney
Attorney-At-Law

I'd like to tell the story now of John Costello Gurney.
By 1948 he was West Fitchburg's first attorney.
A man of great experience, a paragon of knowledge,
With law degrees from Portia Law, and Calvin Coolidge College.
He served in both world wars and knew the shock of cannonade.
He led the Vets of Foreign Wars in the Armistice Parade.
Grand Master of the Knights, he was, a Justice and a Notary,
He never missed a meeting of Kiwanis or the Rotary.
He'd speak at civic functions, and from memory recite,
"The Tragedy of Camelot" as though he were the knight.
And then he'd sing an Irish song, "My Olde Collera Hat,"
Do Shakespeare, Edgar Allen Poe, or "Casey At The Bat."
He looked the squire's part as well: nice clothes, gray haired and slim,
We knew that he liked Ike and it was said that Ike liked him.
He had influence in Boston, and in Washington had pull.
A man of many parts he was; a man whose cup is full.
He had married Kate McNulty in a love match made in heaven,
And Mary Ellen came along in 1937.
They say he went to Boston for a week, and drank and cried,

When the doctor said, in giving birth, that Kate McNulty died.
He collected Mary Ellen, and he moved back from the brink,
A prayer would get him through the day, and through the night—a drink.
He was Fitchburg's best attorney when he was sober as a monk.
He was second best attorney when he showed up on a drunk.
But now, about his daughter, who was Mary Ellen Gurney,
And Chuffa Shea, the local boy, who sent her on that journey.
Young Mary Ellen was the apple of her father's eye,
And all the boys just stood and stared when she went walking by.
She had a smile to penetrate the darkest gloom of night,
She dressed up like a model would—and oh, that girl was bright!
She was a Celtic princess, and she had this golden glow,
We said she was kid sister to Miss Marilyn Monroe.
And everyone admired her, and everyone would say,
"Why does Mary Ellen waste her time with the likes of Chuffa Shea?"
For Chuffa Shea was not that much; at sixteen he quit school,
He seemed to think he knew it all—and Chuffa Shea was "cool."
He had a leather jacket and he rode a noisy bike,
He thought that he and Marlon Brando looked a lot alike.
He drifted all around the town; he couldn't keep a job,
And though the kids all liked him, we agreed he was a slob.
Except for Mary Ellen, who was perched upon that chute,
Protected kids will slide down when they sense forbidden fruit.
And so, they started meeting after school, or at the dances,
And thus began the oddest and ill fated of romances.
It lasted through the winter months, and when the winds turned mild,
Mary Ellen told her closest friends; she knew she was with child.
Such secrets always come out, sure as flesh will turn to dust,
For each of us has someone else we know that we can trust.
At last, as always, someone told a prominent attorney,
About his girl, and what a shock to John Costello Gurney.
He spent that night, he told a friend, in agony and hate,
But everything felt better when he had a dream of Kate.
Mark it ever to his credit how controlled he was that day,
When everyone in Fitchburg thought he'd strangle Chuffa Shea.
He called Chuffa to his office, and he asked him man-to-man,

188

Did he care for Mary Ellen? Was he working out a plan?

And Chuffa Shea just fell apart, like someone broke his toy,
What started out as man-to-man was finished man-to-boy.
And John Costello Gurney had another storm to weather.
He went home to Mary Ellen and they worked it out together.
They agreed she'd have the baby, that they'd see the whole thing
through,
With their Catholic faith to guide them there was nothing else to do.
Mary Ellen finished High School before anyone could tell,
Then went off to see her aunt in California for a spell.
She'd have the baby there, and place it in a loving home,
Then she'd come back to Fitchburg, just as all roads lead to Rome.
She'd pick up life where it was left that bleak and wintry day,
But no one counted on one thing: She still loved Chuffa Shea.
So everything was scheduled and it happened most as planned,
And off she went to see her aunt, who'd help and understand.
And the evening that the baby came, she somehow slipped away,
To find a telephone and place a call to Chuffa Shea.
She told him of their daughter—he was interested but cool,
And only then, I think, she understood how she had played the fool.
She called her dad, apologized, and asked if he could maybe
Accept the fact that she would never part with her new baby.
And John Costello Gurney in a solemn, shaky voice,
Told her all along he had been praying for that choice.
He asked about the baby, mentioned all the things he'd bought her,
And told her to rest up, and then come home with her new daughter.
Well, that's almost all the story of the love match and the journey,
Of Mary Ellen, Little Kate, and John Costello Gurney.
I know that Chuffa Shea left town, was never seen again.
They say his trip was sponsored by a group of local men.
And John Costello Gurney came to blossom and to bloom.
And once again his laughter and his presence filled a room.
And Mary Ellen married well, and never moved so far,
That John Costello Gurney couldn't drive there in his car.
The baby kept her mother's name, and grew to study law.

And went through Georgetown Law School filled with wonder and
with awe.
A law degree, some politics, a clerk for Justice Black,
And then, just like her mother, young Kate had to come back.
She worked with Grandpa for a while, and when the old man died,
She kept his name upon the firm through gratitude and pride.
And still the town of Fitchburg had its number one attorney,
The shingle bears the proudful name, "Judge Kate McNulty Gurney."

Nana, Fr. Walter Gary, and the Priest's Murdered Brother

West Fitchburg in the 1940's was a great place to be a kid. We hung around each other's homes and played Monopoly, crashed electric trains, or played poker and blackjack with stacks of chips. We played ball in the streets and on The Flat, as it was called, the big field behind St. John's, the parish grammar school. We took bicycle trips up Mt. Wachusetts ("rises 2006 feet above the surrounding forest") and watched our tires and brakes smoke as we came down the long, winding roads going hell for leather. Then, there were the woods and the little ponds around Pio's Field to play in as well. I'm not sure if it was "Pio's" or "PO's." I think "PO" might have been the initials of the family that owned the land, but none of us actually knew them. No one seemed to mind we were there as long as nothing was damaged. We could explore, play hide and seek, cowboys and Indians, and occasionally fish, even though it was rare that anyone caught anything bigger than hornpout in these cold millponds. There were relatives, friends, and neighbors all around and we never thought about danger—even in the war years. It was a safe place to be.

Then there was the Church, Sacred Heart Church to be exact. The Church and St. John's Grammar School were a big part of the neighborhood social scene. There was always something going on in one of the two places, populated as they were by a pastor and four priests in the rectory and some fourteen nuns living above the school. There were Sunday and Holy Day Masses, novenas, benedictions,

First Fridays, Lenten Services, Holy Week, Advent, retreats, prayer groups, confessions, not to mention weddings, funerals, baptisms, and confirmation. On the social side, there were committees, school events, auctions, minstrel and variety shows, parents' associations, record hops, and enough work around the several buildings to keep a gang of kids busy on a regular daily basis.

My first paid job at the age of 12 was locking the church four nights a week. I worked for Mr. Nicholas the janitor and in return for these four golden nights he could take off to spend with his friends at The British-American Club, I got twenty-five cents a night—or a dollar a week. Not bad money for a kid in the late Forties.

The job, of course, was terrifying. The church was open until 9pm each night and it was rare to come and lock up without finding several of the older parishioners there, deep in personal prayer and meditation. At my mother's instruction, I started out softly—by blowing out any candles on the altar that looked gutted and in danger of dripping hot wax that might start a late night fire. If that little display of closing etiquette didn't work, I would start putting out some of the lights on the side altar and rattling the side doors to make sure they were properly locked from the inside. That usually did it. One by one the faithful made their final prayer of the night, smiled and waved at me, then headed home. It was like Nana's tale of the old Irish pub cry at closing time: "You don't have to go home, but you can't stay here." In this case, however, it was to their homes they were headed. They would all be back the following morning at 7am for the early Mass.

Alone now in the near dark, I would start to move a little faster. I would lock the three front double doors and then—with my father's trusty army surplus flashlight, walk around the dark outside perimeter of the church, checking windows and side doors. It was a test of nerves. A closed and locked church at night brought back memories of the banshees and ghosts in Nana's stories who were trying to find rest. I used to worry, where better for them to find that rest then right here, around this church, tonight, with me looking after them. Walking through the little cemetery plot in front of the church where the first pastor was buried didn't help my attitude either.

One night, as I made my rounds toward the back of the church, I found the boiler room door unlocked and partly open. Mr. Nicholas forgot to close and lock it after the coal men delivered the several tons of coal that had filled the air with a black cloud of coal dust that took hours to settle. The open door was for ventilation. I knew that. It was up to me to check inside the boiler room, make sure everything was all right, and then relock the doors. "That's what you're paid for, so do it," as my father used to say. I opened the door and went inside the boiler room.

The furnace at this time was still coal powered. It took an enormous furnace to heat that big church, and it took a good man to keep it stoked and operating properly. Some of the parish men volunteered to keep it stoked weekends for Confession and Mass but for the rest of the week the job fell to Mr. Nicholas. It was one more duty in a jam-packed schedule of things to do when one man must maintain a church, school, convent, rectory, and the surrounding outside grounds. I used to think the man would work himself to death. He told me once he made $25 a week for six and one-half days work—plus the three evenings he locked up himself. That didn't sound like much to me, now or then.

The boiler was huge and filled the great furnace room with little space to spare. It was a three-story room with one story dug downward into the floor, a pit, and then two more stories above ground level. Mr. Nicholas said it was built by the same company that built the boilers on the Titanic and was "…only a little smaller." There were ladders all around it to reach the pipes and controls on top. It was a piece of heavy-duty machinery to respect and admire.

I flashed my light around the room to make sure all was well, muttering my little sexton's prayer ("Please God, don't let me see nothin' scary"), and started toward the door—when the furnace started.

I have never heard a noise like that before or since—and that includes the tank range at Ft. Knox. Those old boilers started with a contained explosion that surely should have taken the roof off the building and vaporized any 12-year-old boy and his flashlight that were within a half-mile. I think I was lifted off my feet by the concussion—or maybe I just jumped that high. Whatever happened, I was terrified. I dropped the flashlight and headed for the door, my feet scarcely touching the ground. I made it home in something less than two minutes and took another five minutes calming down before I could tell my mother what happened. "The hero," she smiled, echoing Nana's classic expression "The hair-o," referring to someone of great courage. "Come on," she said. "We'll go back and get your flashlight and make sure the church is locked." And that's what we did. The boiler was running now like the great machine is was and although loud it was nowhere near as terrifying as it had been when it exploded the silence away. Besides, this time I had company. Nothing is as terrifying as it might be when you have someone with you who cares. We checked everything out, collected my father's flashlight (none the worse for being dropped) and went home. I was back on the job the next night. I told my father that going up there alone bothered me and he gave me another of his reassuring insights: "Put it out of your head and it won't bother you."

I only got into trouble one time at Sacred Heart Church. That had to do with Fr. Walter Gary who heard confessions every Saturday afternoon from 3:30-5pm and in the evening from 7-8:30pm. The problem was…well, let me tell it the way I wrote it down several years later:

1947: Father Walter Gary Hears Confession
Sacred Heart Church—West Fitchburg
Saturday Confession
3:30 to 5:00PM & 7:00 to 8:30 PM

Catholic kids all know the pain of Hell and joy of Heaven,
So Saturday confessions were the rule in Forty-Seven.
And you better plan to be there, or the next week - run for cover.
The nuns would march you down from class, boys one week, girls the other.
You'd think a Catholic neighborhood that's filled with kith and kin,
Didn't make for many chances—but the clever kids found sin.
Or thought they did, the point is moot, what matters is design.
Each Saturday the pews were filled, and each priest had his line.
Well, nearly every priest that is, for all of us were wary,

Of giving any sinful news to Father Walter Gary.
It wasn't just the goodly father's booming baritone,
For though he tried to hear you, he was deafer than a stone.
So Saturday was news day! Come you in and sit you down!
And wait for Father Gary's Biggest Little Show in Town!
Psst! Look out, that old nun's watching; kneel and contemplate your
sin,
And stayed wrapped in meditation 'til a stranger walketh in.
One just came in—he looks around, from votive lights to shrines,
And notes that every priest—but one—has lengthy waiting lines.
He goes to Father Gary—to the Scourge of Sacred Heart!
And as he kneels,
I think he feels,
His whole world come apart!
"I'll say the Ten Commandments," Father Walter Gary yells,
In a voice that swamped the statues in a flood of decibels,
"You just stop me as you need to with the listing of your crimes,
Then I'll count off the numbers and you say how many times!"
And Father Gary roared it out—and everyone could hear it.
And people thought about their pride, and not the Holy Spirit.
I'm sure that Father Gary, in his solitude sublime,
Never thought the souls he pardoned there were pardoned just that
time.
He never saw them skulk outside his penitential den,
As rattled, broken hulks the Church might never see again.
But what was that to little boys, whose only business there,
Was in learning who did what to whom, how many times, and where?

What *really* happened is that the old nun turned me in. She
told my mother what my friends and I were up to, and I got a lecture
about that. Nothing too serious, mind you, but a lecture on respecting
the privacy of others. Nana was there too, and she did comment that
someone should have a talk with Fr. Walter Gary as well. No one
ever did, of course. We all grew up with the admonition from the
nuns, "Touch not God's anointed." That meant you never gossiped or
spread scandal about the clergy's behavior. They were responsible

only to the hierarchy and—eventually—to God. Not a particularly good bit of advice as I look back on it, but there it was.

Just so the whole thing would not be a waste, Nana asked if she had told me about the man who murdered the priest's brother in Ireland. I said she hadn't. I would have said that anyway, but in this case it was true. She sent me to fetch hot tea and buttered Graham Crackers, and then told the story of:

The Priest's Murdered Brother

"There was a village in Ireland, not me own, mind you, but we knew about it anyway, where there was a fine old priest who worked hard and was loved by all. He was alone in the world except for an older brother who was not well and who came to live with him for his final days. The priest, Fr. George, was a strong man who felt he could do both his priestly duties and care for his older brother at the same time. He asked the parishioners if they would mind his taking the older brother Leo into the little cottage they provided for him. Sure no one could object to anyone taking care of an older family member, that's what family is for. The approval came back at once and the older brother Leo moved in with Fr. George and it was done.

The older brother turned out to be a worker, despite his age and health. He was a handy man and soon had the little cottage as fit and trim as any in the village. There was even a neat little garden out front. The cottage was the pride of the neighborhood.

That's when the talk started. A few people who knew little and talked much said, 'There must be money there to have such a fine cottage. Perhaps the brother is rich? Or is it the priest who has the money given to the church for his own use?' Humph, as if the few pennies people could put in the baskets mattered one way or the other when, in fact, much of that was given back to the people of the parish that needed it anyway.

One night, when the priest was out on sick calls, a bad man broke into the cottage. He tried to make the brother tell where the money was hidden—but the poor man could tell him nothing, for there was nothing to tell. The bad man hit him with a fireplace poker and the brother, Leo, fell down dead. The bad man, terrified at the evil thing he had done, dragged the poor brother's body to his trap and carried it to a bog where he buried it in a shallow grave.

When the priest returned home, he saw the blood and the marks of a great struggle, and knew what must have happened. He summoned the villagers and they looked high and low for the brother Leo, but they found neither hide nor hair of him. The bad man who did the killing joined in the search and acted as concerned and sorry as the others so he might be considered as innocent as they. May God give him His full justice!

As I say, nothing was found and within a few weeks people had resolved themselves to knowing nothing would ever be found and life came back to as normal for Fr. George as it ever would be again.

Then one Saturday, at confession, the bad man came to Fr. George. 'I am confessing to you, Father,' he began, 'that I killed your brother Leo. I didn't intend to at the start, I just wanted your money, but he fought and I did kill him anyway, so there it is.'

'How dare ye come to me and tell me that?' the startled priest said. 'Ye murdered my own dear brother? How can I forgive ye such a great sin in the sight of God and man before you have confessed to the authorities and received your punishment before the law?'

'I care little for your forgiveness,' said the man, 'but I do want your silence. Now that I have confessed the sin to ye, ye are forbidden by your own Seal of Confession from saying or suggesting anything that would move the blame toward me. Ye are caught up in your own oath and can say nothing.'

And with that, he left the confessional, with Fr. George holding his head and moaning with the pain and torment of it all.

Of course, the bad man was right. Fr. George could do or say nothing to suggest he knew the man who had murdered his brother. The burden vexed him by day and tortured him by night—but there was nothing to be done.

Worse yet, the bad man made himself out to be the priest's friend. He would meet Fr. George on his daily walks and go quietly beside him as the priest held himself in check and read from his Holy Office. Surely, the bad man thought, no one could suspect murder of the man who walks beside the priest.

Fr. George prayed long and hard for guidance, but the answer was always the same. The Seal of Confession may never be broken. The whole matter was hopeless to the poor priest. It seemed that justice would never be done.

One day, many months later, the priest was taking his walk around the outer parts of the village, near the bogs, when the bad man joined him once again. Fr. George ignored him and said nothing, as usual, just read his Holy Office and prayed for strength. After walking in silence for some time, the bad man said aloud, 'That's where he is, you know, over there in the bog, near those shrubs.'

'Where who is?' asked Fr. George, looking up slowly from the reading of his Holy Office.

'Your brother Leo. That's where he is, over there near that bush by the peat bog. That's where I put him after I fought with him and killed him in your cottage with the poker from the fireplace.'

'Ha, ye wretch!' cried Fr. George, wrapping the man in his strong arms. 'So ye killed my brother, did ye? Ye said that out here in the open with no Seal of Confession to hide your evil behind this time. Ye have no claim on me at all—and it's off to the authorities ye'll be going for the justice of man before ye face the Creator and the justice of God.'

And with that, he marched the fellow off to the constable where he reported what the man had said that day—and that day only. The villagers went back with Fr. George to the bog. They searched until they found his brother's body, preserved by the peat to look just as it did the day he died. They brought the poor man home and gave him the Christian burial he deserved. Fr. George himself said the Mass and laid his brother's body to rest in the church cemetery.

And as for the bad man, he was found guilty of murder and punished by the law, may God have mercy on his soul if He can.

And that's how Fr. George found justice for his brother Leo without ever breaking the Seal of Confession.

Now it's almost time for my programs. Give me another cup of tea like a good boy and go think over what I told ye."

Nana, Agnes Daley, and Agnes, The Witch of Lixnaw

My mother, Kathryn Ware McManus, was a lot like her own mother, Mary Dunne Ware, whom all of us knew as Nana. Mother was a good soul, a salt of the earth type, who made friends easily and kept them forever. She worked hard, made few excuses but lots of sacrifices, and was always there for the ones who needed and counted upon her. She took care of her family, including Nana Ware who lived with us, and was a loyal and dependable friend to those who called upon her.

West Fitchburg was such an insular community during the 1940's that almost all of mother's friends were old friends. These were the people who were born in the neighborhood, attended grade school together, socialized and dated among themselves, and when they finally married and settled down it was often just a few streets over from where they had been born—with someone next door they had known in grammar school. My mother Kathryn and my father Leo, for example, met when they started first grade at St. John's Grammar School in Sacred Heart Parish somewhere around 1910. The same St. John's that Mary, Leo, George, and I attended some thirty or more years later. With more than a few of the same old nuns still on the active duty roster, I might add.

One of mother's oldest friends was Agnes Daley. Agnes never married and lived with her brother in the same house in which she was born. Agnes had worked all her life for a local engineering firm and was financially comfortable as she approached middle age.

But, as I learned later, she was very lonely. She came to our house a lot. We had one of the first television sets on the street, a black and white RCA twelve-inch console that cost some $350.00 in 1949 dollars. Agnes was with us several nights a week to watch her favorite shows with mother—mostly Arthur Godfrey as I remember, and he was on just about every morning as well as two or three nights a week. Mother always enjoyed her company.

Agnes was also there when I was sick with rheumatic fever. I was confined to a downstairs bed and Agnes came over each day to play cards with me, read books, talk, make tea and visit with Nana, and generally give my mother a break and a chance to get out of the house. While I napped, Agnes would visit with Nana and talk about the old days and what was going on in the neighborhood, and catch up on family gossip. They thoroughly enjoyed each other's company. Nana told me once that Agnes would have given a lot to have a home and family like we had where something seemed to be going on at all hours of the day and night. "Busy people are happy people," as Nana liked to say.

But a life of family and home was not ordained for Agnes Daily. It was her fate to walk a different road altogether. A road that was nearly incomprehensible to the men of West Fitchburg—but not to the women. It took a little prying and a lot of years, but eventually I learned the story of Agnes Daley and her lonely journey.

1945: Agnes Daley, My Mother's Friend

The holidays pass slowly when you're 50 and alone.
There's no one at the front door and there's no one on the phone.
Your friends are all with family, and off to see their kin.
The ones you like are spending time where strangers don't fit in.
And that's why Agnes Daley felt, with longing and with fear,
That November was the hardest of a hard and lonely year.
If only for a chance, she thought, before the year would end,
To find herself an honest man, a lover, and a friend.
But this was in West Fitchburg back in 1945,
Where every man was taken who was decent—and alive.
So it hurt too much for laughing, but it made no sense to grieve,

200

And Agnes looked ahead to one more lonely Christmas Eve.
She wasn't unattractive in her low-key, homey way,
And her job at West's Design Labs brought her in a handsome pay.
She was Personal Assistant to the senior Dr. West,
And for 27 years she was the brightest and the best.
She knew when Wall Street needed help, they turned to West's
Design,
And Dr. West and staff would help improve their product lines.
The doctor was a thinker, who saw many years ahead,
And the biggest names in industry took note of what he said.
Security was tight at West's for all these complex reasons.
But Agnes Dailey came and went as freely as the seasons.
Well, early that November, at the Shamrock Social Club,
Agnes joined in with her friends to start the social season's hub.
They laughed and they told stories, and they sang a song or two,
And the brightest of the circle was the newcomer named Lou.
He had the purest tenor that the group had ever heard.
He made everybody laugh with an expression, or a word.
His clothes were tailor-made, and in his buttonhole—a flower.
He danced like Fred Astair, and looked a lot like Tyrone Power.
Lou played a mean piano, and he strummed the ukulele,
And often times he seemed to sing and play for Agnes Dailey.
And so, they talked about their lives—they both lived all alone.
And what they liked, and where they'd been, and people they had
known.
They talked away the evening, and they walked home hand-in-glove,
And Agnes had to tell herself—it wasn't really love.
The next two weeks they spent their time together every day,
And Agnes found a balance in her life for work and play.
She dressed a bit more stylish, and she looked both svelte and
slimmer.
Lou stayed with her the weekend that she cooked Thanksgiving
dinner.
The first week of December was a dream within a dream.
A spring appeared in Agnes' step, and in her eye a gleam.
She dreamed again the fairy tales that she had stored away,
Of a wedding in a chapel on a Saturday in May.

201

But then, after the second week, it happened, as she feared:
The people at the Shamrock said that Lou had disappeared.
He hadn't talked to anyone, just left her a short letter.
He said he was in trouble, and that leaving might be better.
He said he really cared for her, and all his love he willed her.
He doubted he'd be back again; the whole thing damn near killed her.
The third week of December was a time for song and dance,
For everyone but Agnes, who walked through it in a trance.
For Lou was gone, she was alone, there's nothing she could do,
Then late one night her doorbell rang—and on the porch stood Lou.
He couldn't leave, he said, until the two of them were right.
They sat there, just the two of them, and talked away the night.
The trouble he was in, she learned, was with his job and boss.
Since due to West's Design Labs they would face a massive loss.
Unless he learned West's latest plan for Automated Cargo,
He'd lose his job, go broke, or be transferred back to Chicago.
If only he could see that plan, he'd score a massive coup,
He'd stay and settle down, and Agnes knew what she must do.
It was Sunday, before Christmas, and the old guard was all smiles,
As he let her in the office and unlocked the private files.
It was, she said, an errand she was on for Dr. West,
And the fewer people in on it would probably be best.
The guard should keep this quiet, "Dr. West himself said that."
The old man said he understood, and tipped his battered hat.
And now she was alone in there, she didn't waste a minute.
Her pocket book was stuffed with all that Lou said to put in it.
He said he'd only copy it; it all was for the best,
When suddenly the door swung wide—and there stood Dr. West.
And with him was Security, a local cop named Sawyer,
A newsman from the Sentinel, and Pierce, his private lawyer.
"We knew," said Dr. West, "that when Lou Preston came to town,
He had come to steal our secrets, and would try to pull us down.
Lou Preston is a business spy, and just inside the law.
He's stolen and re-sold more plans than half our staff could draw.
We knew he'd get to someone here, no matter what we'd do.
So we let him go and watched him, never thinking he'd turn you.
"You know, of course, you're fired and your service here is ended.

I won't press for legal action on the person I've befriended.
Don't say a word, just leave my plant, and never dare come back.
My saddest memory will be of giving you the sack.
The story will go public and get printed in the papers.
Our neighbors like to read about intrigue and tawdry capers.
"And by the way, we learned of Lou from another damaged party.
His wife and their four kids live just outside of Cincinnati."
And Agnes Dailey turn and left, a blank look on her face.
She went and packed a bag and disappeared without a trace.
It was two days after New Year's that the Fitchburg Sentinel read:
"Miss Agnes Daley, 50, found in Cincinnati dead."

Even Nana Ware found it difficult to talk about Agnes Daley after that. "Agnes was a good woman," Nana might say after one of her Rosary prayer sessions, "and let no one judge her but her God." And as for Agnes' false friend? He got unusually strong words and the short shift Nana felt he deserved. "Ah," she spat, "the likes of him. Taking advantage of a good heart and a strong need, and not a "daycent" bone in his body. I would have scratched his eyes out like I did to the picture of the Kaiser when my boys went away to war! God forgive me."

It was time to change the subject. "You knew another Agnes, Nana. Remember when you told me about the old lady in your village they called Agnes, The Witch of Lixnaw? Whatever happened to her?"

"Ah, indeed I knew Agnes, the friend of my girlhood." Nana said smiling and settling back in her chair. Why don't you go fix us a cup of tay and the buttered Graham Crackers and I'll tell ye about the end of Agnes, The Witch of Lixnaw."

The End of Agnes, The Witch of Lixnaw

"Sure, none of us knew how old Agnes was. My mother said Agnes was around the village when she was a little girl—and Agnes seemed to be old then too. That would have been around 1840 when my mother, Mary Kate, remembered old Agnes, walking about, picking up the colorful little stones she loved to collect in her purple bag, and with a smile and a kind word for everyone she met. She was everyone's favorite old woman, she was.

The children called her The Witch because she lived alone and she was a little bit odd, but they knew she was good through and through. She used to make the little clothes near the window in her neat little house and since she had no children of her own we used to say she made them for the Little People. Of course, she really made them to sell or to barter or in some cases, just to give away. I had more than one good dress meself that had been hand made by Agnes, The Witch of Lixnaw.

Well, as we grew older we young ones soon knew that there was little to keep us at home in our neat little village of Lixnaw. There were no jobs there for the men, or women. As the young men heard from their family and friends about the opportunities in America, they left for the new country. The women had to decide if they would stay and lead the spinster's life, or go on a great adventure in the new world and see what their God and His Blessed Mother had in store for them.

In my case, it was an easy choice. My mother had died young and my father took to his sick bed and made me promise to go off to my uncle in America as soon as he died—which seemed closer than either of us wanted to believe. Old Fr. Kavanaugh told me the same thing. 'Mary,' he said, 'there is nothing here for ye. Ye can be my housekeeper forever but I think God has a plan for ye with your uncle in America. Follow your father's advice. Go to your Uncle Tim and see what happens, and God be with ye.'

My father died soon after that. My sisters decided to stay in Ireland, but I knew my father's wish and Fr. Kavanaugh's view. Like so many others, and so many times before, I went to talk the matter out with Agnes.

Everybody in Lixnaw talked with Agnes. Ye went to her little cottage and she'd fix the strong tay and bring out her warm bread with the homemade butter and jam, and she'd stuff ye to your heart's content and all the while she's looking right into your eyes, and smiling and cooing, making ye say even more than ye meant to at the start. She was that good. And when I was all done and asked her what she thought, she took another long sip at the tay and said, 'It doesn't matter, dear, what I think. It's only what ye think that matters. Ye know there is nothing for ye here—except maybe to grow old like me and in another few years when I'm gone, they could be calling you Mary, The Witch of Lixnaw.' I started to tell her that we all knew she was no witch, but she just smiled and patted my hand. 'Never ye mind,' Agnes said. 'There is no disgrace to it. I have had a long and gentle life and if I had no family of me own, I had the sons and daughters of everyone in the village that came to me, as their parents did, for good talk and friendship over strong tay and buttered bread. I have no regrets. I have a few pounds set aside for my old age, and my needs are simple and my friends are generous with their time and help. I know that when I go to my God, St. Patrick will be there to welcome me as an old friend. Maybe God Himself will say, 'Well done, thou good and faithful servant.' I want no more than that.'

'Ye don't plan to go there soon, do ye?' I asked her. 'Ye are one of the last ties we all have to the old days.'

Agnes laughed. 'Ye don't plan things like that, my dear. God does the planning and ye do the obeying. But yes, I think it will be soon. And like your own father, God rest him, I think ye should go to your uncle in America and start your new life. It won't be an easy life, mind ye. It never is for the likes of us. But it will be the life ye were meant to live. Now, go get ye prepared and come back one last time to kiss me goodbye.' And with that, she bowed her head and went all quiet and I knew it was time to go.

It didn't take too long for everything to fall into place. My father and his brother had been writing about me coming over there for some time. Uncle Tim cabled me the thirty dollars it took to book my passage across, and another few dollars to cover food and necessities. It was clear I would have to work it off when I got there, but I expected no less. Fr. Kavanaugh had seen many a villager off before so he knew about the papers and where to go and who to see. He went as many of the places with me as he could to make sure I was treated with respect and courtesy. He was a fine, big old fellow who took nonsense from no man. All the arrangements went easily with his help. Within several days I had the ticket, the papers, and my Gladstone bag that had belonged to my father, packed with the few things I had to take with me. Fr. Kavanaugh gave me his blessing. 'I must go now to say goodbye to Agnes,' I told him. 'I haven't seen her in the village for a few days,' he replied, 'I will go with ye.'

Agnes' cottage was a short walk outside the village and we walked there together as old friends do—quiet in our own thoughts and comfortable with the good company. When we came to the cottage door, he rapped. 'Agnes,' he said, 'it is Fr. Kavanaugh bringing Mary Dunne to say goodbye to ye.' There was no answer. He gently pushed open the door. He called to Agnes again, and we went inside. Her little kitchen area was neat as a pin, and her wooden dinner table with the two hand hewn chairs was drawn up and the table set as though ready for a meal.

'Agnes, are ye up?' he called. We walked to the other little room Agnes used as a sewing and bedroom. There she was, in her chair. Looking for all the world like she was asleep. Fr. Kavanaugh took her hand and bowed his head. 'She is dead, child,' he said. 'Agnes is with her God at last.' I turned away to wipe the tears as Fr. Kavanaugh put his hand gently on old Agnes' head and said a short prayer for her soul. As I looked up, I saw an envelope on her little sewing table with my name written on it in Agnes' neat script. 'Open it, child,' Fr. Kavanaugh said. I did that. Inside was a ten pound note, probably the savings she had told me about, and a handwritten letter that said, 'God Bless Ye, Mary, and bring ye happiness in the new world. Remember me and tell my stories.' It was signed, 'Agnes, The Witch of Lixnaw.'

'And remember her, I did, and I told her stories too. Happy she must be to know that a little boy like ye knows all about Agnes, The Witch of Lixnaw.

The end. Did ye like that story?"

Nana's Sayings

     Nana had a collection of old sayings, or aphorisms, with which she flavored her every day conversation and all the stories she told. These sayings were more than just clichéd shortcuts of speech. They introduced a cultural, religious, and historical comparison that gave status and importance to the conversational exchange. Although she may not have known the specific linguistic terms, Nana understood well the differences between connotation and designation. If for example, your simple breach of trust or act of disobedience was compared to Judas' betrayal of Christ, you knew that what you considered a minor sin was grave indeed. I remember my mother Kathryn used many of these exhortations to excellence too. She used them frequently and to good effect. I suspect that like myself, she picked them up from Nana Ware. I worked as many of these aphorisms into the book as I could without distracting from the story Nana was telling. This little compilation of Nana's sayings is just what the family and I remember and is included purely for fun. You probably have heard many of them before. A few you may read for the first time. I bet you find yourself using some of them!

1. *The Kiss of Judas!* This was used occasionally with three brothers who might insincerely promise to be good, or to accomplish a certain task on time if left to themselves—and then offer to seal the bargain with a kiss.

The Nana In The Chair, And the tales she told
An anecdotal biography of Mary Dunne Ware (1860-1956)

2. *Even a cat may look at the Queen.* This egalitarian saying was used defensively with people who suggested that some friend or family member was rising above their station by hobnobbing with the higher social classes. The Irish were notorious for criticizing their own—and Nana did not approve.

3. *He didn't lick that off the grass!* This has to do with inherited tendencies. The sins of the father (and mothers) are indeed vested in the son (and daughter).

4. *It keeps him out of the bars.* This was used to defend a man's use or misuse of his private time. An example might be a man who had a hobby or athletic interest they pursued extensively in their free time. Anything was better than hanging around the bars.

5. *You don't have to be holier than the Pope.* My favorite. It was used against the occasional priest, nun, or self-proclaimed holy person who urged us to a more rigid religious discipline than the Church itself demanded.

6. *The ones we taught.* This was used toward children who were offering inappropriate opinions and otherwise acting in a too sophisticated or supposedly adult fashion.

7. *There's no fool like an old fool.* This was used to describe a grownup that should have known better than to do, or say, whatever they did or said.

8. *God keep ye simple.* This was used to guide young people who just said or did something incredibly dumb (Example: "I didn't think he'd hit me just because I made fun of his clothes!")

9. *Run! Run like the hounds of the pack are nipping at your heels!* What a marvelous image! An exhortation to speed it up or pick up the pace. May be used when calling a child, or sending them on an errand.

10. *The kind of Catholic who'd send for the doctor before he sent for the priest.* A description of a Catholic whose faith in the healing power of the clergy was at best lukewarm. Some lukewarm Catholics thought you should minister to the body before you prayed for the soul.

11. *I'd hate to be dying and send you for the priest!* A variation of the above. Used toward a slow moving child as an inducement to move faster. It wondrously linked the concept of rapid movement to responsibility for someone's eternal Salvation.

12. *Never, dog, never!* Rarely used, and in those few cases used only against world figures. It suggested some betrayal of Faith or Country (Example: Mother heard it used during World War I against the Kaiser Wilhelm. I remember its usage in World War II when someone repeated Hitler's demand that we surrender lest he invade us).

13. *Whether they be the squire's lady or Rosy O'Grady.* A plea for gender equality. All women should be treated as ladies and with appropriate respect regardless of their station in life.

14. *All decked out like Lady Astor's pet horse.* In the early 19th Century, Lady Astor was known to gaudily bedeck the horse that pulled her coach. Nana used this analogy to describe someone who was overdressed for the occasion.

15. *He's a good old horse!* The ultimate compliment one could pay a hard worker. In Nana's social and hierarchical order, the family members and hard workers were at the very top, and the people who hung around bars were at the very bottom.

16. *As Irish as Paddy's Pig.* Now why Paddy's Pig was the touchstone for Irish authenticity, I know not to this day. However, there it is.

17. *Leave it for the sweeper.* Said to one who just dropped a coin.

18. *May it physic ye.* Admonition to a child who just hogged the limited supply of whatever treats Nana intended all to share in. Not a pleasant thought, but appropriate to the crime.

19. *The lazy man's load.* Said of someone who tried to save multiple trips by carrying everything at one time. It was usually reserved for those instances when something was dropped, lost, or broken.

20. *She's a healthy girl—if a bit plain, but a good worker.* Said of a young woman who might be a bit on the heavy side and perhaps less than attractive. The good worker part was clearly her major asset.

21. *Speak up dear, and don't mumble:* Nana was hard of hearing and if you read her a story, you might hear this presentation advisory.

22. *The prayers of the wicked availeth nothing.* One of two favorite Biblical quotations, this one was used to dismiss a curse or bad wish as when one child might say to another, "I hope you die!"

23. *The guilty fleeeth where no one doth pursue.* The other favorite Biblical quotation. The one was used when a child started adamantly denying responsibility (or guilt) long before it was alleged. Brother Leo remembers a variation: *The guilty dog barks first.*

24. *Ah, don't let them work you to death.* Said seriously to an adult on their way to their job in the mills, or a little mockingly to a child who complained about being summoned into the kitchen to dry the dishes.

25. *Well, we won't get the bread baked (field plowed, etc.) sitting here, will we?* The quiet interlude is over. It is time to move on.

26. *The Workers and The Shirkers.* In the final analysis, these are the two categories into which all of us must fit. I need not point out which one we must aspire to.

27. *Here's your hat, what's your hurry?* Nana told of the old Irish woman whose husband's friends would visit him at home of an evening and overstay their welcome. Well, at least as far as the wife was concerned. The wife slyly suggested they leave in these subtle words. Nana thought it was a great joke. One might hear this if one was running late for Mass or for school.

28. *Jason, Jason, get the basin! Oops, flop! Get the mop.* This one came from a proper upper-class home, back in Nana's house servant days. The wealthy homeowner, with a delicate stomach (I assume), would summon his man Jason—who apparently never arrived in a timely fashion. This was yet another inducement for children to move faster when on an assignment.

29. *Out in the weeds.* Not paying attention. If one's mind drifted while Nana was talking one might hear, "Are ye listening child, or are ye out in the weeds?" It was also used in reference to people who didn't have a clue as to what was going on around them. Another nice mental image.

30. *He holds the lantern while his mother chops the wood.* Yet another inducement to help out a bit more. This was primarily my mother's and used when her son sat by and rested instead of pitching in to get the appointed task accomplished. I bet she heard it from Nana years before.

31. *Good manners are no burden.* There is always time to say please and thank you and getting things done in a civil fashion takes no longer than being rude and boorish.

32. *Make a little story out of it.* Nana appreciated stories that had a beginning, middle, and an end. If you offered a few out-of-

context factoids ("I saw Miss Forbes today and she was upset"), this would be Nana's response.

33. *And these are the Golden Years?* Another favorite of my mother's in her later years—and another hand-me-down from Nana Ware. I suppose if you worked hard all your life, you thought of the Golden Years as a chance to slow down and smell the flowers. It doesn't often work out that way. We knew it was a bad day when we heard this one. This was about as negative as it got.

34. *If wishes were horses, beggars would ride.* Nana was a great believer in the power of prayer. She frequently quoted the theme line of her favorite radio show, The Sacred Heart Hour: "More Things Are Wrought by Prayer than This World Dreams Of." However, there was a great difference in her mind between the efforts of praying and mere idle wishing. Anyone who overused the wishing process in her presence should expect to hear this mild admonition.

35. *The Hero (pronounced "Hair-o").* Another dual usage term. This was sometimes used to question the credibility of a young person's advisor. If one told Nana that their friend Tommy thought it was okay to skip a Sunday Mass to play ball, for example, she might reply, "The Hair-o." This meant one was putting too much confidence in the judgment of another young person. It was used in the sense of, *Consider the source* (a variation). The term was also used to note the faint-heartedness of the young. If one was asked to go down into the cellar and bring up some household supply and one declined to do so because of the dark, one might also expect to hear, "The Hair-o."

36. *Nothing is solved by a broken heart.* This was a call to action. If one cried and sunk into self-pity for too long a time, Nana would say this. It was understood to mean, "Don't just sit there and cry about it. Do something!"

37. *No rest for the weary/No rest for the wicked.* This little advisory was adjustable based on the subject person. If the visiting priest, for example, mentioned he was tired from making his First Friday rounds, he would be favored with the "Weary" version. A young partygoer, on the other hand, who complained about being tired from an overactive social life, could expect the "Wicked" version.

38. *Shank's Mare*: A mode of transportation (i.e. "to walk"). "How will I get these grocery bags back from the store?" Answer: "Shank's mare."

39. *Little Friend*: Another Nana-ism with two meanings. It was used lovingly with a child ("Come give me a hug, Little Friend.") If it was used to refer to an adult, it suggested that they had room for improvement in the maturity department.

40. *The Machine:* This was what Nana called an automobile. "Your father's fine machine," referred to our 1938 Packard 120. It is a 19th century term once used interchangeably with "horseless carriage." Her son, my Uncle George, carried on the historic tradition. When his namesake, my brother George, bought his 1953 Ford Fairlane Convertible, Uncle George referred to it as an "open car." I liked that too.

41. *The second wife wears the diamonds.* There weren't many divorces in West Fitchburg at this time, and the term "Trophy Wife" had not yet been invented. However there were a few widowers around who seemed interested in marrying younger women. In Nana and mother's view, the first wife did all the work and the second wife reaped all the benefits. The "diamonds" part is a bit of an exaggeration among this blue-collar social set. See also *There's no fool like an old fool.*

42. *(Ye/He/She/They) had little to do.* An observation on a pointless, unnecessary, and maybe even mean-spirited event. Perhaps you said something unkind to a family member and they were hurt by it. Maybe you did something really stupid like painting pictures

on the linoleum floor with red nail polish, or sawing the backyard swing seats in half to try out your father's new saw. It conveyed the sense of "Grow up."

43. *I'll whale the tar out of you!* Neither Nana nor my mother (or my father, for that matter) ever laid a hand on me in anger—but this expression was the ultimate threat. My mother used it occasionally to deal with misbehavior in public. It was always set in a future time frame: "I'll whale the tar out of you...when we get home." Nothing ever happened, of course, but it got her through a stressful moment when she had to say something—and caused me to realize I had incurred her wrath.

44. *I bet your pardon. I grant your grace. I hope the cat, will spit in your face.* This little exchange supposedly came out of another fine house where the housekeeper would express umbrage by saying to the junior maids in a very upper class way, "I beg your pardon?" The girls among themselves would later fill in the last two lines. Nana repeated this as a little joke whenever anyone served up the first line.

45. *Offer It Up For The Holy Souls:* This was the way to deal with pain in a Catholic household of the 1940's. Unless you were actually unconscious or in danger of bleeding to death, you were advised to offer up your suffering to shorten the sentence of those poor souls serving time in Purgatory. This, of course, was long before Purgatory was closed after Vatican II.

46. *God bless us and save us and send us the rent.* This ejaculation neatly straddled the sacred and the profane. God's blessing and salvation received top billing, of course, but the realistic needs of daily living were high on the list as well.

47. *There are no pockets in a shroud.* We've all been told that we can't take it with us, but this neat turn of the thought suggests that even if we tried, there are no pockets in a burial garment to carry it anyway.

48. *Ye'll be late for your own funeral.* Often used with small boys who were habitually late for church, school, and with the 3:30pm tea and buttered Graham crackers.

49. *That's the one we're looking for.* The last one. This usually refers to a job of some kind. When we came to husking the last ear of corn, for example, "That's the one we're looking for." It means that the job is almost done.

50. *Careful, lady, careful.* In retirement, old Mattie put on his best clothes and sat by the trolley stop in nice weather. When ladies went on, or got off, the trolley, he would doff his hat and say, "Careful, lady, careful." It was pronounced "Keerful, lady, keerful." It was his contribution to public safety and became a family tag line. Whenever one was engaged in a delicate act, such as removing a sliver or threading a needle, Nana would say...

51. *Your Sainted (Grandfather):* Any departed relative was, by definition, in Heaven. Therefore, one could properly refer to them as a saint. It was occasionally used with a departed friend's name, but more often the friend got a lesser but still important tribute and prayer: *Your sainted grandfather's good friend, Pat. God rest him.*

52. *Pushing Up Daisies:* There were several ways of referring to the dearly departed. If the previous thought covered family members and friends, this expression was used toward the departed to whom one was at best neutral. It seems to suggest that at last the person has a job they can handle.

53. *Wisha, Wisha, Wisha.* I thought this little commentary, which was used apropos of nothing, meant "I wish, I wish, I wish." However, the Dublin Language Board on the Internet says that it was just conversational filler, along the lines of "...like, you know."

54. *Whist let ye!* This was an upscale version of "Shut up!" more along the lines of, "Be quiet, won't ye?"

55. *Cock Mothera!* This meant, "to bollix" or a "cock-up." It anticipated terms like "SNAFU" ("Situation Normal: All Fouled Up.") It was a considered judgment that whatever happened was about as balled up as it could possibly get.

56. *Bad 'Cess To Ye!* This was used not as a curse but as a warning. I'm not sure what "Cess" means exactly, maybe "success"—or lack thereof. The expression referred to luck or fortune—and you'd have a store of bad fortune if you did something bizarre like miss Sunday Mass or talk back to your parents. Her father, Michael, had his variation we heard. "Tamper with the forts and ye'll never have another day's luck."

57. *Laziness, shall I e'er offend thee?* Yet another commentary on work not properly done. The curse of short-cuts. If one was given a chore, such as washing the kitchen floor for example, and one mopped only the middle of the floor, and/or never moved table or chairs, one could expect this classical observation. I'm still looking for the source. It had the flavor of, "I guess I've seen everything now."

58. *Your cup is full.* Nana expected family members to come visit her around the holidays. She also thought the gift of a few bucks was appropriate as well. This expression and the one that follows deal with those two expectations.

   If someone did not show up for a seasonal visit, next time they came around they could expect to hear Nana say, "I missed ye." This was a mild rebuke. If one apologized and cited a near-death reason for not visiting, the matter was over with a pat on the hand and a "Never ye mind." If, however, the family visitor thoughtlessly suggested they had in some way been too busy to visit, or cited such things as conflicting social engagements, they heard Nana say, "Your cup is full." This was her version of the modern, "What a crock."

59. *I got what Paddy got when he shot at the loch.* As indicated above, Nana thought the gift of a few bucks was appropriate from a visiting adult relative. A fiver slipped into her hand at the end of a visit brought a warm thanks and a blessing. My mother would always check with Nana after the visitor left. "What did they give you?" mother would ask. Nana would either hold up her prize or use the above expression.

As I grew older, one of my jobs was to deal with the many Valentine's Day, St. Patrick's Day, Birthday, Easter, and of course Christmas cards she received from both family and friends. We had our ritual: I would open the envelope and hand it to her. Nana would remove the card, open it, and feel inside for the hoped for enclosure. If there was one, she'd hold it up and say, "What 'tis it?" I would say the denomination, and she would smile and offer a little blessing. If there was nothing in the card, she'd sometimes shake the envelope over her lap—just to be sure. Then she'd hand me the card and say, "Read it."

As for Paddy and his Loch, Loch is Gaelic for lake. It is usually associated with Scotland but it is used in Ireland too. I suppose when Paddy shot at the loch, he got no return for his effort and a faceful of water for his trouble.

There is one other possible interpretation: The 19th Century expression in Ireland for a zero point Cribbage hand was "Paddy shot the loch." What it originally meant in that context though is still a mystery.

60. *Lace Curtain and Shanty Irish*: Like many Irish immigrants of her day, Nana felt racism first hand. There were indeed signs reading, "No Irish Need Apply" on the hiring offices at some of the mills. The Irish were often considered unstable and drunkards. A judgment that deprived them of a chance to earn a living and sometimes made them unstable and drove them to drink. Nana remembered a little jingle that non-Irish children would sing to the tune of an Irish jig:

"Have you ever been into an Irishman's shanty?
Where money is scarce but the whiskey is plenty,

A two-legged stool at the end of a hall,
A picture to cover a hole in the wall."
Racial expressions abounded, including "Paddy Wagon"
for the police van that supposedly rounded up the drunken
Paddy's after a raucous Saturday night, and "Irish Confetti" was a
brick (supposedly thrown at weddings, just before the brawl
started).

It was a little better in Boston where there was at least a
veneer of civility. Nana worked there early in her life as a
domestic in one of the finer Irish-Catholic houses. These wealthy
and educated Irish had been in America for many years. They
were the "lace curtain Irish." They were the assimilated and
successful Irish, and were generations, miles and mindsets away
from their country cousins in the mill towns who would be forever
the "shanty Irish."

61. *He says more than his prayers.* This little observation was
occasionally made of someone who told a story that boggled
Nana's imagination. She wasn't suggesting that anyone was
playing with the facts, mind you. She simply observed that not
everything coming out of a person's mouth could be accepted
with the purity of a prayer.

62. *Touch not God's anointed!* I heard this from Nana, my mother,
and the nuns. It meant that we could not comment or tell negative
stories (even if true) about the clergy. They were beyond us and
whatever they did was "between God and themselves." This is
probably the single worst piece of advice that ever came out of the
Church. It bred a clerical culture that caused some of them to
believe they were above the law and that they could, and did, get
away with anything. Actually, this biblical remark never applied
to the clergy. It had to do with the murder of a king. The prophet
used these dramatic words to admonish that an anointed king
should not be murdered.

63. *One for each hand*: A special reward for good conduct and
occasionally, just for being the "good child that ye are." It meant

you get a double treat: Two cookies, or two pieces of candy, "one for each hand."

64. *There's temptation in steel*: As far as Nana was concerned, a pair of scissors or a knife of any sort was an unsuitable present for a family member or friend. *Sharp edges sever ties.* Such a gift could bring enmity between two otherwise close people. So—for example, if you gave a boy a jackknife for his birthday, you extracted a payment of one cent, a penny. That way you weren't giving him the knife, you were selling it to him. And that made all the difference in the world.

65. *God helps the needy, not the greedy:* One was expected to be grateful for the blessings they were given. We are given not what we ask for, but what we need. That said, if one received a gift and wished only that it could have been a bit more, they could expect to hear this observation.

66. *We'll just add a little water to the soup*: An indication of hospitality and welcome. If someone showed up to visit around meal or teatime, that would be invited to stay and eat with the family. They might demure, saying, "But you weren't expecting me." Nana or my mother would say this to indicate it was no bother at all.

67. *Come-All-Ye's:* This was pronounced as one, three syllable, word. It referred to the old Irish songs Nana sang and loved. I don't know the derivation of the term, but a musical friend suggested it came from the first line of many old Irish war songs. They often began with an exhortation to arms like, "Oh, come all ye brave Irishman, and answer to the call…"

68. *In and out like a fiddler's arm:* I heard this as a small boy running in and out of the house for drinks, snacks, and bathroom use. It showed minor irritation with constant door banging and interruption, but was usually said good naturedly. I also heard it

used about a certain family member who was not proficient at keeping a job.

69. *We're all alike at the end:* One of Nana's frequent prayers was for a happy death. When her time came, she wanted to go peacefully, with her priest and her family around her. To a large extent, this prayer was granted. Nana used this little expression to communicate that no matter how important we became in life, nor how high our expectations became, at the end of life we all wanted the same thing: Freedom from pain, peace of mind, the expectation of a better life, and our family around us.

70. *You don't have to be Irish to be thick, but it helps.* This observation came forth when someone in the family, or in the closest circle of friends, did something really stupid. Nana supported her family and friends in all cases and without hesitation. However, she reserved the right to make her feelings known from time to time.

71. *If there is a remedy find it, if not never mind it.* I guess this means there's no sense wasting your time worrying about the itch if you can't reach it to scratch. The secret to getting things done was, and is, just keep moving.

72. *If it doesn't bother you, don't bother it.* This incorporates both the old saw about letting sleeping dogs lie, and the one about not fixing what ain't busted. There are enough real problems in life, she seemed to be saying, without needlessly creating any new ones.

73. *Neither be the first by whom the new is tried nor the last to set the old aside.* In the computer world they used to say, "Never buy Rev 0 of anything. It won't work." Nana presaged that high tech warning by about sixty years.

74. *It's hotter than the hinges of Hell.* This was one of my mother's favorites, although I heard it a time or two from Nana. It was

perhaps on an August afternoon without a breath of air to be found inside or out. It was also used to describe home made soup. I remember Nana calling out once from her room as she sampled a bowl of Mom's famous chicken soup, "Glory be to God, Kathryn, it's hotter than the hinges of hell!" I like the image of the door to Hell sporting wrought iron hinges that reflected the ambient temperature inside.

75. *Up the back of the head*: This expression was accompanied by a gentle swipe up the backside of a little boy's head. It was intended to get his attention—along the far more extreme lines of having to hit a mule with a two-by-four to accomplish a similar end. Most times it was replaced with its alternate: *Hit your head*. In other words, "I want your full attention. Listen to me."

76. *Next parish over*: A long way away. During the Irish diasporas in the late 1800's, so many Irish immigrated to Boston to find freedom and escape poverty that they jokingly referred to Boston as "the next parish over." Nana used the term to refer to a great distance away and also to the city of Boston itself, which was fifty miles east of Fitchburg. Nana told us how the local Fitchburg gentry would get a write-up in the local society pages whenever they made a trip into the city. A trip from Fitchburg to Boston was a great adventure and a newsworthy event.

77. *I'm dead waiting to be washed*: I'm exhausted. In rural Ireland the women of the family would wash the deceased loved one's body before inviting neighbors in for the wake. My mother, Kathryn, carried this expression on from Nana's collection of sayings. She used it to express a low point in the day where she not only felt dead, but the family hadn't even got around to washing the body.

My (Other) Grandmother's Clock

Before I close, I must give a little more time to the McManus side of the family. As I said, I did not know many of these people except through the family stories my father told and handed down. My Grandmother Mary Ellen (Lally) McManus died when my father was young, and my Grandfather Felix died when I was two years old in 1939. However, my father kept their memories alive with his stories. I mentioned the time he played lookout for the men from the mill that played cards in the woods on their way home from work on a payday. Felix found out about that and marched him home with a switch. Then there was the time during Prohibition when my father's employer, the pharmacist Tommy L'Esperance, had a grand idea to make money. He had a big, heavy 1927 Cadillac that he had souped up and modified to accept a second large gas tank in the undercarriage. This second tank, however, was intended to hold bootleg whisky. My father's job would be to drive it into Canada as though for a tourist visit, have it filled with the bootleg stuff, and then drive it back across the border. No one would ever know, and he'd be handsomely paid for his efforts. Felix found out about that grand idea too and put an end to it as quickly as he had ended the lookout adventure. My father's stories were fun and always made the point that you could never in his day, and still couldn't in my day, do anything in West Fitchburg that your parents wouldn't find out about in one way or another. He was right. It was the ultimate police state in that every relation and family friend was a potential informer. You might as well behave. It was simpler all around. Many kids opted out of wild ideas by simply saying, "Naw, I'm out. My old man would find out and kill me." Everybody understood that.

One of my father's favorite tales was the story of his mother Ellen's clock. It was a Seth Thomas eight-day mantle clock with a faux marble base, elaborate brass legs, and a round face with black Gothic numbers. It was the centerpiece of my grandparents' home. It was a gift from Felix to his bride, Mary Ellen, on their wedding day in 1892. It sat on top of the dining room china closet in the white house on Temple Street for as long as I can remember. Mary Ellen cared for it until her death in 1917. Blanche cared for it only a year before she died in the great influenza epidemic of 1918. Felix cared for it until his death in 1939. My father took responsibility for it in 1939 and cared for it until his death in 1990. I have had it since then. My son Timothy has volunteered, and been approved, as the next custodian of Grandmother's Clock. It will be his responsibility to decide who gets to care for it next. As I write this in 2003, the clock is in wonderful condition and keeps perfect time.

I had the clock appraised once by an antique clock specialist. It is worth only a few hundred dollars despite its age and remarkable condition. The dealer told me why: "Seth Thomas made their clocks so well that even now, one hundred and fifteen years later, there are still many working models in homes and antique shops around the country. A working Seth Thomas clock from the 1880's is just not that rare." How's that for a product testimonial?

This old Seth Thomas mantle clock was an integral part of growing up in the house on Temple Street. I grew up with the ticking and chiming of that grandmother's clock. If I was at home on a school day afternoon, it quietly and unobtrusively drove my schedule: Nana's Ware tea was served promptly at the stroke of 3:30pm. Homework started at 4:30pm. My father came home from work at 5:30pm. Nana used to listen to the clock during the long nights when sleep would not come. "I heard the clock strike 3 this morning," she might say, "and I hadn't shut my eyes yet." My father once said the clock timed Mary Ellen and Felix's life, his sister Blanche's life, and now it was timing his life. I guess today it is timing mine.

However, there is no subject so serious that you can't have a little fun with it. We used to play clock games. When I was sick with rheumatic fever, I was confined to a chaise lounge in the dining room, right under the old clock. My father, mother, Nana and others used to think up questions about the clock in an effort to amuse and challenge me. I have since played these games with my children and now with my grandchildren in more recent years. Grandson Kevin is the best so far. He can usually figure out the answers in the shortest time. Let's try a few and see how you do:

Here's all you need to know to answer all the questions. Given: The clock strikes the hour and then again strikes one on the half hour. It does this twenty-four hours a day. That is all you need know. Here are the questions:

1. How many times a day does the clock strike three?
2. How many times a day does the clock strike two?
3. How many times a day does the clock strike one?
4. How many times does the clock strike noon?
5. I woke up last night when the clock struck one. What time was it?
6. Again last night, about a half hour after the clock struck one, it struck one again. What time was it?
7. And yet again last night, about a half hour after the above, it struck one again. What time was it?
8. In any 24-hour day, how many times does the clock strike?
9. If you counted thirteen strikes—what would be the likely reason?
10. Moving the clock ahead one hour in the spring for Daylight Savings Time is easy, but clock experts warn against moving the hands back one hour in the fall when we return to Standard Time. The hands on these old clocks were not designed to move backwards. Why didn't they consider Daylight Savings Time when they manufactured these clocks?
11. There are two ways to set the clock back one hour when changing from Daylights Savings to Standard Time. What are the two ways?

Think about it and then check your scores against five generations of McManus and Wares.

Answers:
1. Twice. The clock strikes three o'clock twice each day: Once in the am and once in the pm.
2. Twice: Same as above: The clock strikes two, once in the am and once in the pm.
3. Twenty-Six: The clock strikes one twenty-six times each day: Once in the am and once in the pm. It also strikes one on each half hour. That's twenty-four plus two or twenty-six.
4. It strikes "noon" just once. It also strikes "midnight" just once.
5. You can't be sure. A single strike could be 1am or any half hour.
6. You can't be sure, but the field is narrowing. If the first ring was at 1am then it is now 1:30am. However, if the first ring was at 12:30am the second strike was 1:00am. You need to stay awake another 30 minutes and listen to what happens.
7. It is now 1:30am. Three single strikes a half hour apart could only mean that the first was at 12:30am, the next was at 1:00am, and the final strike was at 1:30am.
8. One hundred and eighty strikes each day. That's one through twelve at twice each (156), plus those twenty-four half hour single strikes.
9. If you counted thirteen strokes, it could only be because you miscounted. A striking clock cannot strike thirteen.
10. Because there was no Daylight Savings Time when the clock was designed and built. Daylights Savings Time was introduced in the 1940's, many years later.
11. The two ways to set the clock back one hour are: 1. Move the hands ahead 11 hours. The clock does not distinguish between am and pm so this will put the time one hour behind its previous setting. 2. Easier yet, stop the clock.

Return one hour later and restart it. You have effectively moved the time shown back one hour.

If you had eight correct answers or better, you have been "using your squash" as my father would say. If you got all ten correct you should buy an old Seth Thomas mantle clock of your own. You can enjoy its company while you think up questions to befuddle, challenge, and entertain children and grandchildren of your own. The clock will amuse and keep you company - while it times your life. But at least it will be open about it. It will loudly note the passing of each hour, and after all, everything has its cost, doesn't it?

A Parting Shot

The story poems about the people who populated West Fitchburg and my early days were "worked in" because they are stories that I think add texture to the times. Besides, I had fun writing them and wanted to share them with anyone interested enough to read my book. I hope you enjoyed them and found them an enhancement to understanding the people and the times. They are the kinds of stories that Nana loved. I didn't get to tell her all of them but I did show them to her daughters, Kathryn and May, who agreed that they were definitely Nana-Class stories.

I'll close with one more. This is about the local Irish-Catholic Funeral Home that I call O'Reilly's Funeral Home. It existed under a different name, then and now, and many of West Fitchburg's dearly departed Irish-Catholics ended up there for a proper and reverent burial. This story is about the summer I worked there and contains one of Uncle Jerome's favorite stories of the business:

1960: O'Reilly's Funeral Home
Jerome J. O'Reilly, Mortician
"Serving Fitchburg's Catholic Community Since 1900"

When you're discharged from the army, with a wife who is expecting,
And you have no job or prospects—it's no time to be reflecting,
On the cosmic, social issues of the teeming, human mob,
You just get out there among them—and you find yourself a *job.*

The Nana In The Chair, And the tales she told
An anecdotal biography of Mary Dunne Ware (1860-1956)

For a while, you can be choosey ("I had hoped for something better"),
But your checkbook has a slow leak, and the bank sends you a letter,
Now your boat is near the rapids, and you have no oar to row it,
And your wife is getting nervous—though she tries hard not to show
it.
You work a little here and there; the soldier, poet, and scholar,
Works weeknights buffing hard wood floors, to earn himself a dollar.
And finally you get lucky, when your wife's Uncle Jerome,
Offers you a situation at **O'Reilly's Funeral Home**.
O'Reilly's was the Catholic home, the Irish all would use it,
And in fifty years of service, no one ever could accuse it,
Of not providing everything—from rosaries to sherry,
And the Master's eye, which watched it all, was Judy's Uncle Jerry.
A funeral home's a decent place, where decent people work.
But the thought makes people nervous, and they often shrink and
shirk
From seeking paid employment of the men who look so dour,
When meant, in 1960, that they paid four bucks an hour!
"The work," you ask, "What was the work? And please, don't be too
graphic."
The work my skittish friend was this; I was in charge of traffic.
I waved cars in; I waved cars out; and sometimes set up chairs,
And if the priest did not show up, I might have led the prayers.
But the story I must tell you, happened one St. Patrick's Day,
When winds blew cold through lifeless trees, and all was dark and
gray.
When Uncle Jerry waked a former resident of Cork,
Who wanted to be buried with his mother in New York.
New York's 200 miles due west, to drive there takes six hours.
Alone, on a March wintry eve, through snow storms and through
showers,
And Pat, O'Reilly's driver, worked himself into a sniff:
"I'll not drive to New York alone—with just Himself—the stiff."
Uncle Jerry had the Irish way; his talk was smooth as honey.
And the few times that it failed him, he could still fall back on money.
"A Corporal Work of Mercy, Pat, for giftor and for giftee.
And though I'm sure that's quite enough, I'll pay an extra Fifty."

228

And Pat was hooked, we all could see, and now would volunteer,
But he couldn't quite accept it—such a wondrous thing is Fear!
"A wicked man, you are, Jerome—a crafty one and wily,
Just like your father, Rest His Soul, a typical O'Reilly."
"I'll drive the stiff to New York then, God knows I am not prone,
But my final, firm condition is—I'll not go all alone!"
"It's done!" says Uncle Jerry, "Fitchburg State's just up the street,
And there's always some young college kid who'll take the second
seat."
"Now you go home, get rested, and come back here late tonight,
The hearse will all be loaded up, and parked beneath that light.
The college boy will be all set, just use your key and go.
And get away quick as you can, I think it looks like snow."
And Uncle Jerry did it all; the Case was packed and vanned,
Now the climax of my story comes from sources second-hand.
The college boy came early, and the night was dark and deep.
So he opened up the hearse rear door, crawled in, and fell asleep
Pat came an hour later, and he started up the hearse,
Then he sat another hour, and he cursed an Irish curse.
'The college boy will be there,' Bah! It's starting in to snow.
And if I'm going to make it, on my own, I'd better go."
He clutched and slipped it into low, the Caddie's engine roared,
He couldn't hear the kid in back, who comfortably snored.
He headed down Route Two on his delivery to New York,
His last night late assignment, with the little man from Cork.
It happened on Route Two, I think; Pat had to use the brake,
When he creased a nasty pothole and the schoolboy came awake.
He parted the side curtains; saw the roadside speeding by,
He realized what had happened—and he had no alibi.
He crawled up toward the driver's seat, and opened the partition,
While Pat's attention was engrossed on accomplishing his mission.
Without a thought, he put his face, near Pat—and with a cough he
Signaled he was there and asked, "Would you like to stop for coffee?"
The Cadillac had power brakes, so when Pat stomped and froze,
The hearse went ninety yards on just two wheels, and its chrome nose.
Pat left it there abandoned, near the Devens/Shirley fork.
The Caddie hearse, the college kid, and the little man from Cork.

229

The State Cops came got Jerry, and they opened up the road.
He tried to calm the college kid; the Cadillac was towed.
They moved into the back-up van, and headed for New York—
Just Uncle Jerry, all alone, with the little man from Cork.
Pat showed up some days later, never said where he had been,
But his nerves were mostly gone, they say, he'd never drive again.
But Uncle Jerry—he went on, and used his charm and guile,
To help his Irish-Catholic friends go out with grace and style.
He hired on the college kid—perhaps to keep him quiet,
And the business? In some twenty years, he let the young guy buy it.
And me? I worked for Bernie Doyle, commuted to New York.
And once we went to see the grave, of the little man from Cork.

#

Afterward

As I told you many times, Nana often ended her stories this way:

"The End. Did ye like that story?"

Well, did ye? Write and tell me. My mailing address is in the front of this book—or email me at ecmcm@aol.com.

About the Author

Edward C. McManus is a businessman/writer. He is the author of humor books, publishes **The Jokesmith**, a comedy newsletter for business & professional speakers, and is a freelance writer. You may reach him at Jokesmith1@aol.com.

Printed in the United States
19799LVS00005B/214-354